Managerial Economics and Operations Research

Managerial Economics
and
Operations Research

A Nonmathematical Introduction

EDITED BY

Edwin Mansfield
UNIVERSITY OF PENNSYLVANIA

W·W·NORTON & COMPANY·INC·NEW YORK

"Industrial Decision-making: Old Style and New" by Alfred P. Sloan: from **Adventures of a White Collar Worker** by Alfred P. Sloan, Jr. Copyright 1940, 1941, by Alfred P. Sloan, Jr. and Boyden Sparkes. Reprinted by permission of Doubleday & Company, Inc.

"The Decision-making Process" by Herbert A. Simon: from "The Executive as Decision Maker" in **The New Science of Management Decision** by Herbert A. Simon. Copyright © 1960 by School of Commerce, Accounts, and Finance, New York University. Reprinted by permission of Harper & Row, Publisher.

"The Comparison of Alternatives" by Eugene L. Grant and W. Grant Ireson: from **Principles of Engineering Economy**, Fourth Edition, Revised Printing. Copyright © 1964 The Ronald Press Company.

"Cost Analysis" by Neil Harlan, Charles Christenson, and Richard Vancil: from **Managerial Economics: Text and Cases** (Homewood, Ill.: Richard D. Irwin, Inc.), 1962.

"The Measurement of Profits" by Joel Dean: from "Measuring Profits for Executive Decisions," **Accounting Review**, April 1951.

"A Note on Break-even Charts" from: February 1949 issue of **Fortune** Magazine by special permission; © 1949 Time, Inc.

"Estimating the Price Elasticity of Demand" by Joel Dean: from **Managerial Economics** © 1951. Reprinted by permission of Prentice-Hall, Inc., Englewood Cliffs, New Jersey.

"Pricing and the Character of the Product" by A. D. H. Kaplan, Joel B. Dirlam, and Robert F. Lanzilotti: from **Pricing in Big Business: A Case Approach** (Brookings Institution, 1958).

"Time Adjustments of Flows of Funds" by Pearson Hunt, Charles M. Williams, and Gordon Donaldson: from **Basic Business Finance: Text and Cases** (Homewood, Ill.: Richard D. Irwin, Inc.), Revised Edition, 1961.

"A Simple Example of Capital Budgeting" by Alan S. Manne: from **Economic Analysis for Business Decisions**, Copyright © 1961 by McGraw-Hill, Inc. Used by permission of McGraw-Hill Book Company.

"Measuring the Productivity of Capital" by Joel Dean: from **Harvard Business Review**, January–February 1954.

"Business and Economic Forecasting", **Business Week**. Reprinted from the September 24, 1955 issue of **Business Week** by special permission. Copyright © 1955 by McGraw-Hill, Inc.

"Economics and Business Planning" by Sidney S. Alexander: from **Economics and the Policy Maker: Brookings Lectures 1958–1959** (Brookings Institution, 1959), pp. 1–26.

"Parkinson's Law" by C. Northcote Parkinson: from **The Economist**, London, November 19, 1955. Reprinted by permission of **The Economist** and Houghton Mifflin Company.

"Operations Research" by Cyril Herrmann and John Magee: from "Operations Research for Management," **Harvard Business Review**, July–August 1953.

Contents

Preface

The postwar period has witnessed exciting and important developments in economics and related disciplines, with the invention or adaptation of new techniques and concepts for solving major managerial problems of business firms, the military services, and other organizations. In the first place, traditional economic analysis has been extended to meet the need for greater precision in the management of the business enterprise. In the process a new field, *managerial economics,* has emerged. In developing a more rigorous approach to executive decisions, managerial economics draws upon economic analysis for such concepts as cost, demand, profit, and competition. It attempts to bridge the gap between the purely analytical problems that intrigue many economic theorists and the problems of policy that management must face. It now offers powerful tools and approaches for managerial policy-making.

In recent years another new field—*operations research* or *management science*—has been opened up. Its boundaries are not easy to define. According to one definition, operations research involves "the use of systematic quantitative analysis to aid in the making of management decisions."[1] Emphasis is placed on a scientific approach to decision-making, with considerable reliance on advanced mathematical techniques and a computer-based technology. First used on a sustained and significant scale in connection with military activities during World War II, operations research has spread rapidly throughout American industry, and is now a very important managerial tool.

1. Charles Hitch, "Economics and Military Operations Research," *Review of Economics and Statistics,* August 1958, p. 200.

This book provides an elementary description of important facets of these new fields. Aimed primarily at students of economics and business administration with modest training in mathematics, it provides a general introduction to the nature, purpose, and potential usefulness of various concepts and techniques in managerial economics and operations research without going far into their technical details. Much material is available for the advanced student with some mathematical sophistication, but little is available for the beginner. Hopefully, this book will help to fill the gap.

The two papers that form the Introduction to this volume explore the nature of the decision-making process. The papers contained in Part Two deal mainly with four broad topics: (1) costs and profits, (2) demand and pricing, (3) investment analysis and capital budgeting, and (4) business and economic forecasting. The papers in Part Three are concerned with (1) mathematical programming, (2) game theory, (3) statistical decision theory, and (4) inventory and queuing theory. The critical role of the computer in modern management and the application of operations research to military planning are the principal topics under consideration in the concluding Part of this volume.

E. M.

Managerial Economics and Operations Research

Part One

Introduction

SINCE managerial economics and operations research deal with decision making, we begin by considering the nature of the decision-making process as it presently exists in most industrial organizations. Alfred P. Sloan describes some of his experiences as a top executive of General Motors and concludes that the great difference in decision-making between today and yesterday "is what might be referred to as the necessity of the scientific approach, the diminution of operation by hunches; this affects men, tools, and methods." Herbert Simon then discusses the various phases of the decision-making process, which he characterizes as: finding occasions for making a decision, finding possible courses of action, and choosing among courses of action.

Industrial Decision-making:
Old Style and New

Alfred P. Sloan

One of America's leading industrialists, Alfred P. Sloan was president of General Motors from 1923 to 1937 and chairman of its board of directors from 1937 to 1956. This short piece is taken from his book, Adventures of a White-Collar Worker.

[When I was vice-president of General Motors and Mr. Durant was president,] I was constantly amazed by his daring way of making decisions. My business experience had convinced me facts are precious things, to be eagerly sought and treated with respect. But Mr. Durant would proceed on a course of action guided solely, as far as I could tell, by some intuitive flash of brilliance. He never felt obliged to make an engineering hunt for facts. Yet at times he was astoundingly correct in his judgments.

One legend concerning him goes back to 1912, when a gathering of automobile manufacturers pooled guesses on the next year's production, each man dropping his slip of paper into a derby hat. That year 378,000 cars had been made. Mr. Durant guessed that in the next year they would manufacture half a million cars.

The others gasped. They said, "People can't buy that many

3

cars. Our industry will be ruined by such overproduction before it really gets started."

Mr. Durant mildly rebuked them, saying, "Gentlemen, you don't realize the purchasing power of the American people. I look forward to the time we'll make and sell one million cars a year."

Those men thought he was being fantastic. Actually, his vision was clear. In 1929 the industry was to make, and sell, 5,621,000 automobiles. However, this example of Mr. Durant's vision does not alter the fact that many costly errors would have been avoided had his practice been to base decisions on a comprehensive analysis of all facts and circumstances. He was invariably optimistic. It was easy to be optimistic, though, if you had been in a position to observe the booming growth of Detroit, Flint, and other places where cars were being made; and Durant had seen all of it. * * *

Although I had important responsibilities under Mr. Durant, our methods of approaching operating problems were entirely different. But I liked him even when I disagreed with him. Durant's integrity? Unblemished. Work? He was a prodigious worker. Devotion to General Motors? Why, it was his baby! He would have made any sacrifice for it, and he did make for it almost the ultimate sacrifice. But the question constantly in my mind was whether the potential industrial force under the General Motors emblem could be realized by the same boldness and daring that had been needed to enlist the units of that force. General Motors had become too big to be a one-man show. It was already far too complicated. The future required something more than an individual's genius. In any company I would be the first to say that William C. Durant was a genius. But General Motors justified the most competent executive group that could possibly be brought together.

In bringing General Motors into existence, Mr. Durant had operated as a dictator. But such an institution could not grow into a successful organization under a dictatorship. Dictatorship is the most effective way of administration, provided the dictator knows the complete answers to all questions. But he never does and never will. That is why dictatorships eventually fail. If

General Motors were to capitalize its wonderful opportunity, it would have to be guided by an organization of intellects. A great industrial organization requires the best of many minds.* * *

After forty years of experience in American industry, I would say that my concept of the management scheme of a great industrial organization, simply expressed, is to divide it into as many parts as consistently can be done, place in charge of each part the most capable executive that can be found, develop a system of coordination so that each part may strengthen and support each other part; thus not only welding all parts together in the common interests of a joint enterprise, but importantly developing ability and initiative through the instrumentalities of responsibility and ambition—developing men and giving them an opportunity to exercise their talents, both in their own interests as well as in that of the business.

To formalize this scheme, I worked out what we speak of in industry as an organization chart. It shows how the business functions from the standpoint of the relationship of the different units, one to another, as well as the authority delegated to the executives, also in relation to one another. I grouped together those operations which had a common relationship, and I placed over each such group for coordinating purposes what I termed a Group Executive. These group executives were the only ones that reported to me. Then I developed a General Staff similar in name and purpose to what exists in the army. The general staff was on a functional basis: engineering, distribution, legal, financial affairs, and so on. Each of these functions was presided over by a vice-president, the purpose being twofold: first, to perform those functions that could be done more effectively by one activity in the interests of the whole; and second, to coordinate the functional activities of the different operating units as well as to promote their effectiveness. In the General Motors scheme, for instance, the vice-president in charge of sales is a coordinating executive. He has a staff at his command. His contribution is in developing better and more advanced policies of distribution technique through research and in other ways.

He cooperates with the sales departments of the different operating units. But he has no direct authority over their operations; that exists exclusively in the chief executive of the operation itself.

There is no need of repeating the story of how Chevrolet grew and grew, until it gained world leadership among the motorcars in the low-priced field, and how it has successfully maintained that leadership.

As I proudly make that observation there comes into my mind a rather interesting incident.

At the time Mr. du Pont became president, someone had the idea of having a survey made of the General Motors properties, with recommendations as to what might be done in the way of a reconstruction program. The job was entrusted to a firm of consulting engineers of high standing. The most illuminating recommendation was that the whole Chevrolet operation should be liquidated. There was no chance to make it a profitable business. We could not hope to compete. I was much upset because I feared the prestige of the authors might overcome our arguments to the contrary. So I went to Mr. du Pont and told him what we thought we might accomplish if we built a good product and sold it aggressively. We urged upon him the fact that many more people always could buy low-priced cars than Cadillacs and even Buicks. That it was an insult to say we could not compete with anyone. It was a case of ability and hard work. He listened most patiently, and finally said, "Forget the report. We will go ahead and see what we can do." Mr. du Pont was always that way. He had the courage of his convictions. Facts were the only things that counted. So Chevrolet was saved and General Motors avoided what would have been a catastrophe.

The great difference in managerial technique between the industry of today as compared with that of yesterday is what might be referred to as the necessity of the scientific approach, the elimination of operation by hunches; this affects men, tools and methods. Many associate the word scientific with physics. But it means much more than that. Scientific management means a constant search for the facts, the true actualities, and their intelligent, unprejudiced analysis. Thus, and in no other way, policies and their administration are determined. I keep saying to the General Motors organization that we are prepared to spend any proper amount of money to get the facts. Only by increased knowledge can we progress, perhaps I had better say survive. That is really research, but few realize that research can and should be just as effectively used in all functional branches of industry as in physics. Research into the problem of distribution, for instance, has paid General Motors big dividends. Again it is the scientific approach. I keep mentioning it because it seems to me the willingness and ability to apply such methods might well determine the extent of success of any enterprise, and the larger the enterprise, the more vital it becomes. I had thought much about all this as an executive working under Mr. Durant; hence it was natural, as chief executive of the corporation, that I should turn to that type of managerial approach. The answer would be found in the facts.

The Decision-making Process

HERBERT A. SIMON

Herbert A. Simon is Associate Dean of the Graduate School of Industrial Administration at Carnegie Institute of Technology. The following paper comes from his book, The New Science of Managerial Decision Making, *published in 1960.*

Decision making comprises three principal phases: finding occasions for making a decision; finding possible courses of action; and choosing among courses of action. These three activities account for quite different fractions of the time budgets of executives. The fractions vary greatly from one organization level to another and from one executive to another, but we can make some generalizations about them even from casual observation. Executives spend a large fraction of their time surveying the economic, technical, political, and social environment to identify new conditions that call for new actions. They probably spend an even larger fraction of their time, individually or with their associates, seeking to invent, design, and develop possible courses of action for handling situations where a decision is needed. They spend a small fraction of their time in choosing among alternative actions already developed to meet an identified problem and already analysed for their consequences. The three fractions, added together, account for most of what executives do.[1]

1. The way in which these activities take shape within an organization is described in some detail in James G. March and Herbert A. Simon, *Organizations* (New York: John Wiley & Sons, Inc., 1958), chapters 6 and 7.

The first phase of the decision-making process—searching the environment for conditions calling for decision—I shall call *intelligence* activity (borrowing the military meaning of intelligence). The second phase—inventing, developing, and analysing possible courses of action—I shall call *design* activity. The third phase—selecting a particular course of action from those available—I shall call *choice* activity.

Let me illustrate these three phases of decision. In the past five years, many companies have reorganized their accounting and other data processing activities in order to make use of large electronic computers. How has this come about? Computers first became available commercially in the early 1950s. Although, in some vague and general sense, company managements were aware that computers existed, few managements had investigated their possible applications with any thoroughness before about 1955. For most companies, the use of computers required no decision before that time because it hadn't been placed on the agenda.[2]

The intelligence activity preceding the introduction of computers tended to come about in one of two ways. Some companies—for example, in the aircraft and atomic energy industries—were burdened with enormously complex computations for engineering design. Because efficiency in computation was a constant problem, and because the design departments were staffed with engineers who could understand, at least in general, the technology of computers, awareness of computers and their potentialities came early to these companies. After computers were already in extensive use for design calculations, businesses with a large number-processing load—insurance companies, accounting departments in large firms, banks—discovered these new devices and began to consider seriously their introduction.

Once it was recognized that computers might have a place in modern business, a major design task had to be carried out in each company before they could be introduced. It is now a commonplace that payrolls can be prepared by computers. Programs in both the general and computer senses for doing this are relatively

2. Richard M. Cyert, Herbert A. Simon, and Donald B. Trow, "Observation of a Business Decision," *Journal of Business,* Vol. 29 (1956), pp. 237-248.

easy to design in any given situation.[3] To develop the first computer programs for preparing payroll, however, was a major research and development project. Few companies having carried
their investigations of computers to the point where they had
definite plans for their use, failed to install them. Commitment to
the new course of action took place gradually as the intelligence
and design phases of the decision were going on. The final choice
was, in many instances, almost *pro forma.*

Generally speaking, intelligence activity precedes design, and
design activity precedes choice. The cycle of phases is, however,
far more complex than this sequence suggests. Each phase in
making a particular decision is itself a complex decision-making
process. The design phase, for example, may call for new intelligence activities; problems at any given level generate subprob-
lems that, in turn, have their intelligence, design, and choice
phases, and so on. There are wheels within wheels within wheels.
Nevertheless, the three large phases are often clearly discernible
as the organizational decision process unfolds. They are closely
related to the stages in problem solving first described by John
Dewey:

What is the problem?

What are the alternatives?

Which alternative is best?[4]

3. For a good discussion on the use of the computer for such purposes,
see Robert H. Gregory and Richard L. Van Horn, *Automatic Data-Processing
Systems* (San Francisco: Wadsworth Publishing Company, Inc., 1960).

4. John Dewey, *How We Think* (New York: D. C. Heath & Company,
1910), chapter 8.

Part Two

Managerial Economics: Concepts, Techniques, and Problems

MANAGERIAL economics is concerned with the application of economic concepts and economic analysis to the problem of formulating rational managerial decisions. The essays in Part Two describe some of these basic economic concepts and techniques and illustrate how they can be useful to the manager. Although the concepts are elementary, they often turn out to be important in pointing up fundamental ways of viewing problems and in showing the way to well-reasoned conclusions.

The first four papers deal with costs and profits. Eugene Grant points out that many managerial decisions are made improperly because the decision-maker fails to reason clearly about the costs of alternative courses of action. To arrive at a realistic cost figure for decision-making, it is necessary to define the alternatives clearly; otherwise, some costs which are common to both alternatives may influence the choice. Grant notes two important corollaries of this: average and marginal costs should not be confused and "sunk costs are sunk." Neil E. Harlan, Charles J. Christenson, and Richard F. Vancil are also concerned with the proper measurement of the costs of alternative courses of action. Using a hypothetical case, they describe the different cost concepts used by accountants and economists, and conclude that the economist's notion of opportunity cost is more appropriate for decision-making than the accountant's notion of acquisition cost. Joel Dean also contrasts accounting and economic concepts but places his emphasis on profits rather than costs. Focusing on the meaning of depreciation, the treatment of capital gains, and the valuation of assets, he concludes that, for purposes of managerial decision-making, a profit statement based on economic concepts is more useful than one based on the conventions of fiscal accounting. His paper is followed by one taken from *Fortune* which describes the break-even chart, the diagram that projects a firm's revenues and costs at various levels of sales. To illustrate its use, two hypothetical cases are taken up.

The next three papers are concerned with demand and pricing. One of the first things a firm must consider in pricing its product is the price elasticity of demand. The editor's paper discusses the nature and determinants of this elasticity and describes why it is of major importance. Joel Dean's paper suggests various ways in which the firm can estimate the price elasticity of demand, using controlled experiments, consumer questionnaires, engineering estimates, and correlation analyses. He describes in some detail a study of this sort done for a large New York department store. Then A. D. H. Kaplan, Joel B. Dirlam, and Robert F. Lanzillotti show how a firm's pricing policy is influenced by the character of its product—the type of demand to which it caters, its physical attributes, production requirements, amenability to differentiation, and stage of maturity.

The following three papers deal with investment analysis and capital budgeting. To solve most investment problems, it is necessary to reduce funds received or spent at different points in time to comparable terms. Because a firm can realize a positive return from the investment of its funds, a dollar now is worth more than a dollar later. Pearson Hunt, Charles Williams, and Gordon Donaldson provide the solutions to various investment problems and show how to compute an investment's rate of return. Alan Manne presents a very simple model of capital budgeting, the process by which the firm chooses among alternative investment opportunities.

In a paper which is now a classic in this field, Joel Dean discusses various ways of measuring the economic worth of investment proposals. He evaluates the three most commonly used yardsticks of investment worth—degree of necessity, payback period, and rate of return—and concludes that rate of return is the best. After discussing some of the mistakes that are made in estimating the rate of return, he describes and illustrates the use of the discounted-cash-flow method of computing rates of return, a method which he regards as "demonstrably superior to existing alternatives in accuracy, realism, relevance, and sensitivity."

The next two papers deal with economic forecasting and long-run business planning. Practically all problems in managerial economics involve forecasting. The decision of whether or not to build a new plant may depend crucially on forecasts of demand. Whether or not to cut price may depend crucially on forecasts of the price of materials. The article from *Business Week* describes the various techniques that are commonly used to forecast economic magnitudes: trend extrapolation, leading series, econometric models, and others. Turning to the role of the economist in a large corporation, Sidney Alexander argues that the economist can make his most valuable contribution in long-term planning.

The concluding paper in this Part is Parkinson's Law. This famous, and amusing, law is based on the proposition that "work expands so as to fill the time available for its completion." Although C. Northcote Parkinson is writing about the British bureaucracy, Parkinson's Law also contains a significant grain of truth if applied to American industry, despite the development of managerial economics and other tools designed to increase industrial efficiency.

The Comparison of Alternatives

EUGENE L. GRANT AND
W. GRANT IRESON

Eugene Grant is Professor of Economics of Engineering at Stanford University. In 1960 he, together with Ireson Grant, wrote Principles of Engineering Economy, *from which this article is taken.*

The conduct of a business enterprise requires a successive series of business decisions—decisions between possible alternatives with reference to the future. These decisions are of all degrees of importance, varying from trivial matters to matters of major policy. Some of them are made by intuitive judgments or "hunches" without any conscious attempt to express the alternatives to be compared in commensurable terms, or perhaps even to see clearly what these alternatives really are. Others, however, involve choices between definite alternatives which have been made commensurable by reducing them to terms of money and time. There is much evidence that many of these latter decisions, based on conscious economy studies involving estimates of expected costs (and possibly of revenues) are incorrectly made because of the failure of the estimator to reason clearly about the *differences* between alternatives which involve common elements.

WHAT IS THE "COST" OF AN AUTOMOBILE TRIP?

To illustrate the type of error that may occur if alternatives are not clearly defined, let us consider a familiar and relatively simple situation. Suppose it is desired to estimate the cost of a 600-mile automobile trip.

Bill Jones, who has agreed to "share the cost" of such a proposed trip to be taken in the car of his friend Tom Smith, may calculate merely the expected out-of-pocket expense for gasoline. If Smith's car makes 15 miles to the gallon, and gasoline costs 25 cents per gallon, this is 1⅔ cents per mile. He therefore concludes that the trip will cost $10.

Tom Smith, on the other hand, may estimate all of the costs associated with the ownership and operation of his automobile over its expected life in his service, in order to find an average cost per mile. His car has a first cost of $2,000; he expects to drive it 10,000 miles per year for four years; at the end of this time he hopes to realize $1,000 from its sale. His estimates of total cost might be as follows:

1. Gasoline (40,000 miles at 1⅔¢ per mile)	$ 667
2. Oil and grease	163
3. Tires	150
4. Repairs and maintenance	600
5. Insurance	400
6. Storage (48 months at $5 per month)	240
7. License fees and property taxes	120
8. Total depreciation in 4 years ($2,000-$1,000)	1,000
9. Interest on investment in car	260
(This is based on average interest at 4% per annum.)	
	$3,600

Divided among 40,000 miles of travel, this is an average cost of 9 cents per mile. At this rate a 600-mile trip appears to cost $54.

The Concept of Cost Must Be Related to Specific Alternatives if It Is to Be a Reliable Guide to Decisions · The second of these two figures for the cost of a given service is 540 percent of the first one. At first glance it would appear that one or the other of the two figures must be wide of its mark. However, a more critical consideration will disclose that the simple question "What is its cost?" with reference to a particular service does not define any mark for the estimator to shoot at.

To use a cost figure as a basis for a decision, it is necessary to have clearly in mind the alternatives between which it is desired to decide. Otherwise, certain costs which, after a clear definition of alternatives, would be recognized as common to both, may be given weight in influencing the choice. It is dangerous to base conclusions on average costs without regard to the specific alternatives which it is intended to compare. The fact that widely differing cost figures may be required for different decisions about a given service may be illustrated by examining some of the different pairs of alternatives which might arise relative to the service of a given automobile.

A Situation in Which It Is Necessary to Estimate Total Cost of Ownership and Operation · If Tom Smith did not own an automobile, and wanted to decide whether or not to purchase one, he might set up the following alternatives for comparison:

Alternative A. Buy a $2,000 car and operate it approximately 10,-000 miles per year for the next four years.

Alternative B. Do not buy a car. Use some others means of transportation as railway, street car, bus, taxicab, his friends' automobiles, and his own legs for part of the contemplated mileage and do without the rest.

If these are the alternatives, all of the items included in his estimate of $3,600 for four years' service are disbursements[1] which will take place if Alternative A is selected, and which will not take place if Alternative B is selected. Thus, the unit cost of 9 cents per mile is relevant to Smith's decision whether or not to own a car. The total cost (which in this case is more important than the average cost per unit of service) of $3,600 should be compared with the costs associated with Alternative B. The higher cost of A, if any, should then be judged in the light of differences which are not reducible to money terms, and in the light of Smith's prospective ability to pay this higher cost.

A Situation in Which It Is Necessary to Estimate the Increment Cost of an Added Service · On the other hand, if Smith has

1. That is, they are all disbursements with the possible exception of interest which might in some cases be a disbursement and in others an income given up—an opportunity foregone.

already purchased an automobile and intends to continue to own and operate it, but is undecided about the annual mileage he will drive, the kinds of alternatives to be compared are quite different. In order to determine the effect on cost of driving extra miles, he might set up two alternatives differing only in annual mileage:

Alternative A. Continue to own the car, driving it 12,500 miles per year for four years before disposing of it.

Alternative B. Continue to own the car, driving it 10,000 miles per year for four years before disposing of it.

In comparing these alternatives, it is necessary to consider the various elements of total cost of ownership which have already been listed, item by item, and estimate the effect on each of a total increase of 10,000 miles in the mileage driven over the life of the car.

Item 1, gasoline, and item 2, oil and grease, may be expected to increase at least in proportion to the increase in mileage. It is likely that the increase would be somewhat more than in direct proportion, because of the tendency of the rate of consumption of fuel and lubricants to increase after a car has been driven a good many miles. Perhaps if the car had averaged 15 miles per gallon in its first 40,000 miles, it might average only 14.3 miles per gallon in the following 10,000 miles. In general, item 3, tires, may be expected to increase in proportion to driving mileage; the actual effect of any proposed increase in mileage will depend on whether it requires the purchase of tires and tubes during the extended period of service. Item 4, repairs and maintenance, will doubtless tend to increase somewhat more than in direct proportion to mileage.

On the other hand item 5, insurance, item 6, storage, and item 7, license fees and property taxes, will be unchanged by an increase in mileage driven in any given time. Because the second-hand price of automobiles seems to depend almost entirely on age and not on miles driven, it is probable that the estimated realizable value after four years will be affected very little, if at all, by an increase of 25 percent in total mileage. If this is the case, neither item 8, total depreciation, nor item 9, interest, will be changed by the contemplated increase in mileage.

Smith might make his estimate of the extra costs associated

with increasing his total expected mileage from 40,000 to 50,000 somewhat as follows:

1. Gasoline (10,000 miles at 1¾¢ per mile) $175
2. Oil and grease   50
3. Tires   50
4. Repairs and maintenance   225
                                                 ————
                                                 $500

If this estimate is correct, so that an increase of 10,000 miles would increase total costs by $500, then the average cost for each increased mile of travel is 5 cents. This unit increment cost might then be applied to the mileage of any proposed trip, in order to get an idea of how the proposed trip will affect automobile costs in the long run. If this is done for a proposed 600-mile trip, the conclusion will be that this trip ultimately will be responsible for $30 of extra expense.[2]

It will be noted that although this estimated unit increment cost of 5 cents per mile is much less than the estimated 9 cents per mile for ownership and operation over the life of the automobile, it is three times the 1¾ cents per mile estimate that Bill Jones made for the out-of-pocket expense of a short trip. The difference between the 5-cent and the 9-cent figures lies in those costs that are "fixed" by the decision to buy and to continue to own and operate the car, and which are, therefore, independent of its miles of operation. On the other hand, the difference between the 1¾-cent and the 5-cent figures is the difference between short-run and long-run viewpoints. It may well be true that the only out-of-pocket expenses of a 600-mile trip will be for gasoline; nevertheless, the long-run effect of increasing the number of miles of

2. Incidentally, it may be noted that the question of what, in equity, Bill Jones ought to pay when he rides in Tom Smith's car "sharing the cost" of a trip is a question of social conduct which cannot be answered by an economy study. All an economy study can do is to disclose the expected differences between alternatives. Thus, if Tom is making the trip in any event, an economy study might indicate that the least he could afford to accept from Bill without loss would be nothing at all; this is the difference between the alternatives: (a) make the trip, taking Bill along, and (b) make the trip, leaving Bill behind. On the other hand, if he is making the trip entirely for Bill's convenience, his estimates would appear to indicate that the least he could afford to take for a 600-mile trip is $30; here the alternatives are: (a) make the trip with Bill and (b) do not make the trip at all.

operation of an automobile will be to increase the expenditures for lubricants, tires, and repairs.

A Situation in Which It is Necessary to Estimate the Costs of Continuing a Machine in Service · If Smith purchases an automobile, and then has misgivings as to whether or not he can afford to continue to own and operate it, the alternatives which present themselves to him are still different, and different cost figures from any we have yet discussed will be required as a basis for his decision. Suppose he sets up the following alternatives for comparison:

Alternative A. Continue to own the car, driving it 10,000 miles per year for four years.

Alternative B. Immediately dispose of the car for the best price obtainable, thereafter using other means of transportation.

In considering the difference between these two alternatives, it is necessary to recognize that the $2,000 purchase price of the car has already been spent, no matter which alternative is chosen. The important question here is not the past outlay for the car, but rather the "best price obtainable" for it if Alternative B is selected.

If Smith's decision had been made, say, in 1947, when it was possible to sell certain makes of new cars in a so-called used car market at several hundred dollars more than the purchase price, this best price obtainable might have been $2,500. If so, Smith's question would obviously have been whether or not he could afford to continue to own an automobile that he could sell for $2,500. On the other hand, if his decision is to be made under the more normal conditions where the resale price of a new automobile is substantially below its purchase price, even though the car may have been driven only a few miles, the best price obtainable might possibly be $1,700. Under these circumstances, Smith's question is whether or not he can afford to continue to own an automobile that he could sell for $1,700. The $300 difference between the $2,000 purchase price and the $1,700 resale price is gone whether he keeps the car or disposes of it at once.

The principles underlying financial calculations to determine whether or not to continue to own a given asset enter into a wide variety of engineering economy studies. . . . At this point it is sufficient to note that there is a substantial difference in principle between a decision whether or not to acquire an asset and a decision whether or not to continue to own and operate that asset once it is acquired. To guide the latter type of decision intelligently, attention must be focused on the net realizable value of the machine (that is, on the prospective net receipts from its sale if it should be disposed of). Once an asset has been purchased, its purchase price has been paid regardless of whether it is continued in service or disposed of at once. This past investment may be thought of as a "sunk cost" that, generally speaking, has no relevance in decisions for the future.

COMPARING ALTERNATIVES IN BUSINESS SITUATIONS

These examples from the familiar situation of automobile ownership have illustrated the necessity for recognizing definite alternatives to be compared before using cost as a basis for decisions. No doubt the different kinds of relevant "costs" which should be considered in automobile ownership and operation are recognized in their qualitative aspects by many automobile owners. However, even in these relatively simple situations which have been discussed, it will be noted that in order to express differences quantitatively we were obliged to make assumptions which, in order to be definite, were somewhat arbitrary. For instance, in order to estimate increment costs per mile of operation, we found it necessary to assume two definite total mileages, and to assume that the four-year period of ownership would be unchanged by a change in the total miles of operation.

In industry, the circumstances in which comparisons are made are likely to be more involved. The machines and structures which are the subjects of engineering economy studies are generally parts of a complex plant, and this complexity may create difficulties in differentiating the effects of alternatives. As has been stated, industrialists are often misled as to the costs which are relevant to particular decisions by failure to define alternatives clearly. In industrial situations, even more than in the automobile cost illustration, it is necessary to make definite assumptions in order to have a basis for decisions.

Irreducible Data in Comparing Alternatives · In the case of the alternatives involving Tom Smith's decision whether or not to purchase a car, we noted briefly that there would be certain advantages and certain hazards incident to the ownership of an automobile which could not be reduced to money terms, but which, nevertheless, would have considerable influence on Smith's choice.

This is characteristic of many economy studies. Although the reduction of units which would otherwise be incommensurable (for example, tons of coal, pounds of structural steel, barrels of cement, gallons of oil, kilowatt-hours of electric energy, hours of skilled machinists' labor, hours of common labor) to terms of money and time is essential to all business decisions which are not made entirely on "hunch," some differences between alternatives will generally remain which cannot be reduced to money terms. In an economy study, it is as much a part of the estimator's duty to note these irreducibles as it is to predict the money receipts and disbursements at various dates. The final decision must give weight to the irreducible differences, as well as to the money differences.

Differences Between Alternatives Are in the Future · If it is recognized that only those matters which are different as between two alternatives are relevant to their comparison, it should be obvious that everything that has happened in the past is irrelevant, except as it may help in the prediction of the future. Whatever has already happened is past and gone, regardless of which of two future alternatives is selected. This implies, among other things, that apportionments against future times of expenditures already past should not be included in economy studies. It also implies that economy studies are based on forecasts, and that their conclusions are dependent on predictions of future events, predictions which are either conscious forecasts or implied ones.

The Limitations of Accounting as a Basis for Estimates in Economy Studies · Generally speaking, the accounts of an enterprise constitute the source of information which has the greatest potential value in making estimates for economy studies. Nevertheless, the uncritical use of accounting figures is responsible for many errors in such estimates. There are a number of important differences between the point of view of accounting and that which should be taken in an economy study.

Accounting involves a recording of past receipts and expenditures. It deals only with what happened regarding policies actually followed and is not concerned with alternatives that might have been followed; it is concerned more with average costs than with differences in cost. It involves apportionment of past costs against future periods of time, and apportionment of joint costs between various services or products. It does not involve consideration of the time value of money.

Engineering economy, on the other hand, always involves alternatives; it deals with prospective differences between future alternatives. It is concerned with differences between costs rather than apportionments of costs. It does involve consideration of the time value of money.

Cost Analysis

NEIL E. HARLAN,
CHARLES J. CHRISTENSON,
AND RICHARD F. VANCIL

Neil Harlan is Professor of Business Administration at Harvard University. In 1962 he, together with Charles Christenson and Richard Vancil, wrote Managerial Economics, *from which the following article is taken.*

Why is cost analysis so important in making business decisions? The answer lies in the objectives of the business enterprise and in the way its accomplishments are measured in our economy.

In a narrow, simplified sense it might be said that business administration consists of the twin tasks of (1) allocating resources among alternative uses and (2) supervising the activities of people to insure that the resources are efficiently utilized toward achieving the assigned goals. While there is nothing wrong with this definition as a theoretical concept, it glosses over the uncertainties of the complex world of business. Business administration is an art. While there have been rapid advances in scientific, professional management during the last half-century, successful business administration still requires an intangible ability best described as *skill*.

The success of a commercial enterprise in allocating its resources effectively is usually measured by the profit it earns, and a primary goal of most firms is, therefore, to earn a profit, either the maximum possible profit or a satisfactory profit consistent with other goals of the firm. But what is profit? Both the accountant and the economist use this word to mean the difference between the revenues earned from the sale of goods and services and the costs incurred in earning these revenues. Yet, despite this agreement on the basic concept of profit, the accountant and the economist would generally disagree if each were asked to measure the profit of a particular business enterprise.

The disagreement would arise primarily because of a difference between the accounting concept and the economic concept of cost, Even here, however, there is an element of agreement: both the accountant and the economist consider cost as a measurement in monetary terms of the resources consumed by the firm in producing its revenue. The accountant usually measures the *acquisition cost* of these resources, in the sense of the money amount which the firm had to pay when it initially acquired the resources. The economist, in contrast, thinks in terms of the *opportunity cost* of the resources. The opportunity cost of devoting a resource to a particular use is the return that the resource could earn in its best alternative use. The economist's concept of cost, therefore, involves an explicit recognition of the problem of choice faced by the businessman in the utilization of resources.

Opportunity cost may be either greater or less than acquisition cost. Suppose, for example, that a firm is considering the production of an item which would require the use of material on hand for which $100 was originally paid; the acquisition cost, then, is $100. If the material could currently be sold on the market for $125, however, its opportunity cost must be $125, since the use of the material requires the firm to forego the opportunity of receiving $125. If, on the other hand, the material currently has no market value nor any alternative use, its opportunity cost is zero.

The businessman lives with both these concepts of cost. For decision-making purposes, the economist's concept of opportunity cost is the relevant one, since a rational decision must involve the comparison of alternative courses of action. The accountant's role as a "scorekeeper" for outside investors is also important to the businessman. Moreover, accounting records are often a primary source of information for decision-making purposes.

Types of Resources · The basic resource of business is money, or perhaps more precisely, the power that money has in our society to command the primary resources, the labor provided by men and the materials provided by nature. Money by itself is power-less, however, without a manager or entrepreneur to decide how to put it to work. Even then, capital does not become productive until it is exchanged for more tangible resources than imagination: labor, raw materials, and combinations of labor and materials in the form of products manufactured by other business. In the "raw" state, as money, the wise utilization of resources is difficult; it becomes even more difficult once the money resource has been exchanged for a wide variety of heterogeneous resources, each with a specialized productive capability.

An operating business possesses a variety of resources in addi-tion to money: a building which is adaptable to a greater or lesser variety of uses, equipment which can be used to produce a range of products with varying degrees of efficiency, and employees whose productive skills may embrace a broad spectrum. At first glance, the problem of allocating physical resources might not seem vastly different from that of allocating money. All of these resources have been purchased with money, and their values can be measured in monetary terms. Why, then, did Henry J. Kaiser, a man with adequate capital resources and a reputation as an efficient shipbuilder during World War II, fail in his attempt to establish a new line of passenger cars in the late 1940's? It is not an easy task to convert raw capital into an efficient combination of productive resources. And the converse is also true: It is very difficult to measure the value of an existing set of productive re-sources in monetary terms.

In the "long run," money is the basic business resource. But business decisions are made in the short run, and money, the best available common denominator for all resources, is an imperfect yardstick. At the core of the broad problem of resource alloca-tion, therefore, is the problem of measurement. Actually, the measurement problem can usefully be broken into two parts for purposes of analysis: (1) what types of resources will be required in order to carry out each course of action being considered? and (2) what is the value (or cost) of the combination of resources required for each alternative?

Classification of Problems · As a practical matter, businessmen rarely refer to their problems as problems in resource allocation. Rather, they say, "I've got a make-or-buy problem," or a "capital expenditure problem," or a "lease-or-buy problem," or a "pricing problem," and so forth. This "specific problem" orientation is not necessarily due to a failure to recognize the resource allocation characteristic of the problem, it is simply an attempt to find a practical way to begin the analysis that will eventually lead to a decision.

Dividing business decisions into problem categories has two advantages:

1. From his prior experience with similar problems in the past, the businessman may have observed the kinds of resources that typically are involved in the evaluation of alternatives, and may be familiar with some of the most common problems in measuring the cost of the resources required. Categorizing the problem facilitates making maximum use of this experience.

2. Some types of problems may be best resolved using analytical techniques that have been developed specifically for that class of problems. Identifying the type of problem thus serves also to identify the techniques which may aid in the solution.

There is a danger, too, in the classification of business problems: the danger of a closed mind that can only follow familiar decision patterns used in the past rather than searching imaginatively for new and better ways to grapple with the problems of today and tomorrow.

FORMULATING THE PROBLEM

In order to illustrate some of the most common problems of cost analysis, let us examine the decision process in a simple example. The Webber Company manufactures industrial equipment in a small plant with fifty employees. A recent increase in orders has taxed the one-shift capacity of the plant, and management can see that the company will fail to meet its delivery schedules unless some action is taken. What should be done?

The first step in analyzing this problem, and the most important step by far, is to determine the alternative courses of action that might solve the problem. The list is longer than one might first suppose. There are three main types of actions which might be taken: restricting the quantity sold to the present capacity of the plant; increasing the plant capacity on a permanent or semipermanent basis; or increasing capacity on a temporary basis. Under each of these broad headings, further actions can be identified, as the list below demonstrates.

1. Restricting the quantity sold by:
   (*a*) Refusing to accept orders in excess of present plant capacity.
   (*b*) Accepting all orders and apologizing to customers when deliveries are late.
   (*c*) Raising prices enough to reduce volume of orders down to present plant capacity.
2. Increasing plant capacity by:
   (*a*) Building an addition to the present plant.
   (*b*) Operating the present plant on two shifts.
3. Providing temporary capacity by:
   (*a*) Using overtime.
   (*b*) Buying some components from another manufacturer rather than making them.

This initial stage of formulating the problem is vital to wise decision making. It is a waste of time to do a careful analysis of three alternatives and to select the best of the three if a fourth course of action which is far better is completely overlooked. Analysis is no substitute for imagination. A few extra minutes devoted exclusively to the preparation of an exhaustive list of alternatives will nearly always be time well spent.

So that the exhaustive list does not become exhausting, the next (and sometimes simultaneous) step in problem formulation is to select those alternatives that merit further investigation. Several alternatives on Webber Company's list may be eliminated in this screening process. Items 1(*a*) and 1(*c*) would have the effect of reducing the demands placed on the factory. If the company had long-run growth in sales volume as one of its objectives, these two actions might be rejected as incompatible with the goal. Even if the company's only goal were "maximization of long-run profits" (as we will usually assume, in the absence of a specific statement of goals), alternative 1(*a*) is not acceptable if the additional product could be produced profitably. The profit effect of raising prices is more difficult to assess. Let us simply assume that we are interested in determining the best course of action at the present price in order to compare it with the results obtainable at a higher price.

Alternative 1(*b*) might appear attractive as a method of accepting the available orders without incurring additional production costs. Evaluation of this alternative should, however, recognize that it involves the consumption of an intangible business resource, customer "goodwill." Depending upon competition and normal trade practices in Webber's industry, it may be that stretching out of delivery schedules is the best solution to the problem. In most industries, however, this practice might be a costly one, and we will eliminate it from further consideration here.

The remaining four alternatives are ways to provide increased production in order to meet the increased demand. It is difficult to reject any of these solutions based only on a cursory analysis. It may be useful, however, to realize that there are major differences in type and magnitude of the resources required for each course of action. Expanding the plant or adding a second shift will cause significant changes in Webber's fixed costs as well as in its productive capacity. Even a second shift is a semipermanent action that involves hiring new supervisors as well as laborers, and may require a heavy expenditure of the vital *management* resource. Neither of these two actions would be wise unless Webber's management believed that the increase in demand was a relatively permanent one.

As a temporary solution to their problem, therefore, Webber's management might decide to narrow their analysis to a choice between alternatives 3(*a*) and 3(*b*), the use of overtime in the plant or the purchase of some components from outside vendors. The selection of either of these solutions can easily be changed in the future, and a few months from now management may be in a better position to assess the permanence of the current spurt in demand.

The final stage in formulating the problem is now at hand. How shall we evaluate the alternatives that we have decided to examine? What is the criterion on which we shall make our decision? A careful restatement of the problem at this point may help us to see the best way to point our subsequent analysis. It is little help at this point to say that we have a problem in resource allocation. It may be of more use to define the problem as "fulfilling our production requirements while minimizing the consumption of our resources." The businessman would say simply, "Which parts, if any, would it be cheaper to buy outside?"

In situations such as this where the decision has no revenue implications (we have already decided to accept all orders and deliver them on time), the best course of action is the one that costs the least. Realizing that we are equating "cost" with "resource consumption," therefore, we may say that our decision rule will be to choose the "least cost" alternative, and may then turn our attention to measuring the cost of pursuing each course of action.

RELEVANT COSTS

Before we can begin a detailed analysis, we need a more precise statement of the alternatives. For this purpose, we will assume that the anticipated capacity problem will arise only in the machining department of the Webber Company. Normally this department does the machining of all the component parts in the Webber product. Most of the parts are produced in small lots and require specialized skills not possessed by many outside vendors. Two parts, however, are produced in rather large quantities and the machining operations on them are routine. Clearly these parts are the best candidates for outside purchase. If they were purchased outside, the machining department would have no trouble making all the remaining components on schedule.

Having identified the alternatives, we must next determine the resources required to execute them. According to engineering estimates, the production of one unit of Part A requires raw materials costing $3.00 and a half hour of the time of a machine operator, while the production of one unit of Part B requires $8.00 of raw materials and one hour of operator time. The purchasing agent, after checking with several vendors, informs us that the Smithy Corporation, a reliable source, will deliver Part A for $4.50 each and Part B for $11.50 each.

The next step is to determine the cost of the resources required.

Earlier we referred to the different cost concepts used by accountants and economists and we argued that the economist's notion of opportunity cost is more appropriate for decision making than the accountant's notion of acquisition cost. Accounting records provide a useful source of cost data, however, and so we will begin by presenting the costs of the alternatives to the Webber Company as its accountants might prepare them; then we will indicate how these accounting costs must be analyzed and modified to reflect opportunity costs.

Accounting Costs · After being supplied with the list of resources required as given above, the accounting department of the Webber Company provides the following schedule of manufacturing costs:

	Cost per Unit	
	Part A	Part B
Prime Cost:		
Raw materials	$3.00	$ 8.00
Direct labor @ $2.00/hour....................	1.00	2.00
Total prime costs..........................	$4.00	$10.00
Factory overhead @ 100% of labor................	1.00	2.00
Normal manufacturing cost.....................	$5.00	$12.00
Overtime premium @ 50% of labor................	0.50	1.00
Overtime manufacturing cost...................	$5.50	$13.00

The accounting department explains its calculations as follows. The purchase of raw materials is, of course, a direct out-of-pocket cost. The machine operators are paid $2.00 per hour and this rate is applied to the time requirements to arrive at the direct labor cost. The total of raw materials and direct labor costs, representing the cost of resources directly consumed in the manufacture of the parts, is called *prime cost*.

Production of the parts would also require the use of certain common resources of the company: plant, equipment, supervision, and the like. The acquisition costs of these resources, called *overhead costs*, allocated to the machining department are given in Exhibit 1. Since total allocated overhead costs are equal to total direct labor costs, a charge of 100 percent of direct labor is made to cover these overhead costs. Finally, if work were done on overtime, an additional cost of 50 percent of direct labor would be incurred for overtime premium pay.

EXHIBIT 1

WEBBER COMPANY

MONTHLY BUDGET FOR MACHINING DEPARTMENT

Direct labor (2,000 hours @ $2.00)		$4,000
Overhead:	Indirect labor—materials handling	$ 300
	Department foreman	400
	Payroll taxes, vacation and holiday pay, pension contributions, and other fringe benefits	900
	Heat, light, and power	250
	Shop supplies	150
	Depreciation of machinery	800
	Repairs and maintenance—machinery	600
	Allocated share of plant-wide costs (superintendent, building depreciation and maintenance, property taxes and insurance, watchman, etc.)	600
	Total overhead	$4,000

If we look at accounting costs, therefore, both parts are apparently cheaper to buy from Smithy than to produce in our own plant—even ignoring the premium paid for overtime work! But we must take a closer look at the behavior of manufacturing costs.

Another classification of manufacturing costs often used by accountants is into *direct costs* and *fixed costs*. This classification is a little closer to the economist's way of thinking about costs. Direct costs include those which vary at least approximately in proportion to the quantity of production. Prime costs are usually direct costs, but not all direct costs are prime costs: some overhead costs may also vary with production. Analysis of the overhead costs listed in Exhibit 1, for example, might reveal the following facts about the behavior of overhead costs under two circumstances: (*a*) at present volume if one man is laid off and parts are purchased outside; (*b*) at the anticipated increased volume, if overtime is used.

1. *Indirect Labor.* One man is employed as a materials handler in the department. If a machinist were laid off there would be no saving in the wages paid to this man; he would just be a little less busy. If the department worked overtime, however, the materials handling function would have to be performed by someone, either the machinist himself (thereby lowering his productive efficiency) or by the materials handler also working overtime.

2. *Department Foreman.* This cost probably would not vary with either a small decrease or small increase in production. The

machining work to be performed on overtime might not require the presence of a supervisor; if it did, the overtime paid to the supervisor would be relevant.

3. *Payroll Taxes, etc.* These costs amount to nearly 20 percent of Webber's expenses for labor and supervision. If a man were laid off, the entire 20 percent might be saved. There would be some increase in these costs on overtime, but the workers would not get more holidays or longer vacations. The variable portion, using overtime, might be 10 percent of the labor cost.

4. *Heat, Light, Power, and Shop Supplies.* These costs are difficult to analyze. There might be an insignificant saving in power if one machine were shut down. On overtime, additional power and light would be required.

5. *Depreciation.* This cost is not a cash expenditure but a pro rata portion of the original cost of the equipment. This cost, caused simply by the passage of time, will not be changed by management's decision to either lay off a man or use overtime.

6. *Repairs and Maintenance.* This expense is made up of two components: routine, preventive maintenance and the repair of breakdowns. The former is the larger expense, and might be reduced somewhat if one machine were shut down completely. The latter probably bears some relationship to the volume of work put through the equipment and would vary for either a decrease or increase in production.

7. *Allocated Plant Costs.* These overhead costs occur at the next higher level in the company, and would not change as a result of a minor change in production volume in the department.

We may now recapitulate the results of our analysis. Direct labor seems to be a useful measure of volume in this department because each man operates one machine and costs that vary in relation to machine utilization will also vary with labor costs. In Exhibit 2, therefore, we have computed the direct overhead cost for each of the two circumstances mentioned above (laying off one man or using overtime).

How variable are overhead costs? The preceding analysis illustrates how difficult it is to answer that question in a practical way. It seems safe to say that overhead is not completely variable, as might be inferred from the accountant's allocation mechanism. Saving $1.00 in labor cost will not save $1.00 in overhead in the machining department. But any further general statement about overhead variability is useless. For decision-making purposes, the most useful answer is one based on an analysis of the specific cost items in the specific situation in which a specific decision is

EXHIBIT 2

WEBBER COMPANY

Overhead Cost Analysis

| | Monthly budget cost | | Variable cost as a % of direct labor cost changes if | |
| | | | | |
Overhead Item	Amount	% of direct labor	one man laid off	overtime used
Indirect labor—materials handler	$ 300	7.5%	...	7.5%
Department foreman	400	10.0	...	...
Payroll taxes, etc.	900	22.5 *	19.1%	10.8
Heat, light, and power	250	6.2	1.0	2.0
Shop supplies	150	3.8	...	...
Depreciation of machinery	800	20.0	...	...
Repairs and maintenance	600	15.0	12.0	5.0
Allocated plant costs	600	15.0	...	...
Total	$4,000	100.0%	32.1%	25.3%

* Stated as a percentage of total departmental payroll, this cost is $\dfrac{900}{4,700}$ = 19.1%. On overtime, it is estimated here that direct payroll taxes would be 10% of wage costs, but would also apply to the materials handler (10% of 7.5%).

to be made. Fortunately, it is possible to gain skill in this kind of analysis, with a concomitant reduction in the analytical time required. This is a skill worth developing, because reliance on rules of thumb or general cost variability classifications is a poor, and sometimes dangerous, substitute for such skill.

Opportunity Costs · The accountant measures the cost of resources consumed in terms of the outlay originally made to acquire them. The economist, in contrast, measures their cost in relation to alternative opportunities for their employment. Let us see how these two concepts differ in the Webber Company example.

On some costs, the accountant and the economist would agree. This would probably be true, for example, of the cost of buying the parts from the Smithy Corporation or the cost of the raw materials if the parts are manufactured. In these cases, the foregone opportunity is to refrain from buying the parts or the raw material, so that the opportunity cost and the acquisition cost would be identical.

It might seem, in fact, that opportunity cost is identical with the accounting concept of direct cost. While there is a close relationship between opportunity cost and direct cost and while they are often identical, there are important differences which must be borne in mind.

We can illustrate this point using the direct labor cost in the company example. The company employs eleven machinists in the machining department; approximately 2,000 hours of production labor are available each month. Before the company's anticipated sales volume increase, these men spent about 1,550 hours per month on machining the special, low-volume parts and used the balance of their time, as available, to turn out Parts A and B. Forgetting for the moment about the increase in volume, how would you decide whether or not to have Parts A and B made by Smithy? Are the labor costs true opportunity costs? The answer depends on what action Webber's management would take if the parts were purchased outside. A total of 450 labor hours could be saved. Would two and one-half machinists be laid off? Such action might mean reducing the range of skills now available in an eleven-man force, and might cause morale problems for the man working a short week. If, in fact, only one man would be laid off, then we should not say that the entire labor cost used in producing the parts is an opportunity cost of the parts. The relevant cost in this situation is the *total* amount of money that will be spent for labor under each course of action. If labor costs $2.00 per hour, the cost would be $4,000 if both parts are manufactured inside, and about $3,660 if one man is laid off and some parts were purchased. Although Webber's accountant would say that $900 is spent each month on machining labor for Parts A and B, the *opportunity cost* of that labor is only $340. The other $560 is spent primarily to maintain a balanced labor force with the necessary variety of skills—skills that may be a vital resource in Webber's overall success.

On the other hand, now that the demand for Webber's product is expected to increase, what is the relevant labor cost in deciding whether to use overtime to meet the requirements? With a 10 percent increase in demand, 1,705 hours per month are needed for low-volume parts and 495 hours of machining are needed for Parts A and B. Hiring a twelfth man might provide most of the 200 extra hours needed, but there is no room in the plant for another machine. If overtime is used, the additional labor will cost $3.00 per hour, or $600. This cost is relevant to the decision because its expenditure depends upon the course of action management selects.

Even in the relatively simple case of direct labor, therefore, opportunity cost is not necessarily identical with direct cost. In the example just considered, opportunity cost was less than direct cost, but the reverse could also be true, as we will demonstrate shortly. While the acquisition cost of fixed resources (i.e., accounting fixed overhead) is neither a direct cost nor an opportunity cost, there may be an opportunity cost associated with employing these facilities in one use rather than in an alternative. This opportunity cost is relevant in making decisions regarding the use of the fixed resources although it is not an acquisition cost.

Opportunity cost, then, depends upon the context of a particular decision whereas direct cost does not. The two concepts are similar enough to create both an advantage and a danger: an advantage in that direct cost can often be used to estimate opportunity cost, a danger in that this process can be carried farther than appropriate.

COMPARISON OF ALTERNATIVES

After the problem has been formulated and the relevant costs determined, the next step in the analysis of a decision problem is to recapitulate the results of our analysis to determine which alternative is least costly. If the problem has been formulated properly and the cost analysis done systematically, this ranking task is a simple one. Illustrative calculations for the Webber Company's make-or-buy decisions are shown in Exhibits 3 and 4.

Exhibit 3 is an evaluation of the alternatives that faced Webber under its "normal" demand conditions, i.e., before the anticipated increase in demand. As a result of our analysis, the most promising alternatives have now been more sharply defined. Only one man would be laid off if any parts were purchased outside, eliminating 170 labor hours per month. If this were done, Webber would then have to buy outside either 340 units of A or 170 units of B. In terms of total costs, the best alternative is to continue to manufacture all our requirements inside. The only difficult cost calculation is the overhead cost. If all parts were made inside, the labor and overhead budgets would be unchanged at $4,000 each per month. If one man were laid off, labor cost would decline by $340 and the overhead budget would fall by 32.1 percent of that amount (Exhibit 2).

An alternative analysis in Exhibit 3 arrives at the same conclusion in terms of opportunity costs. According to the cost accountant's statement on page 31, the "normal" cost of one unit of Part A was $5.00. We have seen that this figure is not useful

EXHIBIT 3

WEBBER COMPANY

MAKE-OR-BUY ANALYSIS

CONDITION NO. 1: NORMAL DEMAND

	Make 500 units of A and 200 of B	Lay off one machinist and	
		Buy 340 units of A	Buy 170 units of B
Raw material costs:			
Part A	$ 1,500	$ 480	$ 1,500
Part B	1,600	1,600	240
Purchased parts	...	1,530	1,955
Direct labor	4,000	3,660	3,660
Overhead costs	4,000	3,891	3,891
	$11,100	$11,161	$11,246

ALTERNATIVE ANALYSIS

	Opportunity cost of manufacturing	
	Part A	Part B
Raw material costs	$ 3.00	$ 8.00
Direct labor—one man	1.00	2.00
Overhead at 32.1% of labor	0.32	0.64
Total opportunity cost	$ 4.32	$ 10.64
Purchase price	4.50	11.50
Saving due to manufacturing	$ 0.18	$ 0.86
Number of units produced in 170 hours	340	170
Total savings	$61.00	$146.00

for decision-making purposes; we are interested in the opportunity cost of manufacturing Part A. To measure opportunity cost, we must answer the question, "What costs (resources) will be saved if the parts are purchased outside?" For Part A, we will save $3.00 of raw material for each unit, the labor cost of one man divided by the units he could produce, and approximately 32 percent in overhead costs related to labor. What costs (resources) will be required to achieve those savings? Part A must be purchased at a price of $4.50 each. The savings are less than the additional cost, indicating that outside purchase is not the cheapest course of action. It is no coincidence that the total saving due to manufacturing is equal to the difference in the total costs of the alternatives as computed in the upper part of Exhibit 3.

Exhibit 4 is a similar set of calculations after a 10 percent increase in demand. The overhead cost increase of $138 was computed in two stages as follows: Variable overhead was estimated as 25.3 percent of labor in Exhibit 2, and this percentage was applied to the $400 straight time cost of the added labor. In addition, indirect labor and payroll taxes (18.3 percent of labor) would vary as a function of cost (not time), so that percentage was applied to the $200 of overtime premium pay. The best alternative is to buy 400 units per month of Part A rather than to use overtime.

We have said that most decision problems are basically problems in resource allocation. Cost analysis is used to solve these problems because money is the best common denominator for resources, and because money is the basic "scarce resource" which the business would like to utilize in an optimal fashion. In the Webber Company's overtime decision it is useful to conceive of the problem somewhat differently. The company has 2,000 hours of machining capacity available, and our analysis in Exhibit 3 has shown that this capacity should not be reduced. As demand increases, Webber's real question is, "How should the 2,000 hours be allocated among the available jobs?" The special, low-volume parts are of first priority, and require 1,705 of the available hours. The remaining 295 hours should be used in such a way as to maximize their value to Webber.

EXHIBIT 4

WEBBER COMPANY

MAKE-OR-BUY ANALYSIS

CONDITION NO. 2: INCREASED DEMAND

	Use 200 hours of overtime; make 550 units of A and 200 units of B	Use no overtime and buy 400 units of A	buy 200 units of B
Raw material costs:			
Part A	$ 1,650	$ 450	$ 1,650
Part B	1,760	1,760	160
Purchased parts	. . .	1,800	2,300
Direct labor—straight time	4,400	4,000	4,000
Overhead costs	4,000	4,000	4,000
Overtime premium	200	. . . .	. . . .
Overhead costs applied to premium pay	138	. . . .	. . . .
Total cost	$12,148	$12,010	$12,110

ALTERNATIVE ANALYSIS

	Opportunity cost of manufacturing	
	Part A	Part B
Raw material costs	$ 3.00	$ 8.00
Direct labor—200 hours	1.00	2.00
Overhead at 25.3% of labor	0.25	0.51
Overtime premium	0.50	1.00
Overhead at 18.3% of premium	0.09	0.18
Total opportunity cost	$ 4.84	$11.69
Purchase price	4.50	11.50
Saving due to purchase	$ 0.34	$ 0.19
Number of units produced in 200 hours	400	200
Total savings from purchase	$138.00	$38.00

In Exhibit 5 we have computed the contribution per labor hour that would be earned by using the available hours to manufacture Part A or Part B. Labor and its related overhead costs are ignored in this calculation since these costs will not change as a result of our decision. They are part of the fixed resources we desire to allocate optimally. We will spend a total of $4,000 for labor and $4,000 for overhead; our decision is to determine *how* to use this capacity. Additional cash resources are required only

EXHIBIT 5

WEBBER COMPANY

CALCULATION OF CONTRIBUTION PER LABOR HOUR

Hours available:

Total	....	2,000
Required for low-volume, special parts	....	1,705
Available for Parts A or B	....	295

		Part A	Part B
Purchase price per unit	....	$ 4.50	$11.50
Raw material cost per unit	....	3.00	8.00
Materials savings per unit	....	$ 1.50	$ 3.50
Number of units produced per labor hour	.....	2	1
Contribution per labor hour	....	$ 3.00	$ 3.50
Cost of adding additional labor hours:			
Labor per hour.................... $2.00			
Overhead at 25.3%.................. 0.51			
Overtime premium per hour........... 1.00			
Overhead at 18.3% of premium........ 0.18			
Total cost $3.69		3.69	3.69
Excess cost per hour of making rather than buying		$ 0.69	$ 0.19
Total excess cost for 200 hours............		$138.00	$38.00

for materials. For every unit of Part A manufactured we will pay only $3.00 for materials rather than $4.50 for the completed part, a saving of $1.50 per unit or $3.00 per labor hour. Manufacturing Part B is even more attractive because we will save $3.50 per labor hour. In order to get maximum value from our scarce resource (capacity), we should manufacture all of our requirements of Part B before we use any of the capacity to manufacture Part A.

Next, we must decide whether it would be worthwhile to buy additional capacity by using overtime. The cost of adding capacity is $3.69 per hour (Exhibit 5). Since this cost exceeds the contribution earned by the labor hours, the use of overtime is not warranted. The last calculation on Exhibit 5 is proof that this method of analysis is consistent with the two methods shown in Exhibit 4.

Optimal allocation of scarce resources is a primary task of the businessman. The Webber Company example is a simple illustration of what is involved in this task.

The Measurement of Profits

Joel Dean

Joel Dean is Professor of Business Economics at Columbia University's Graduate School of Business. This paper is taken from the Accounting Review.

Profits must be measured differently for different purposes, and the kind of measurement that is needed for many executive decisions is not provided by the conventional income statement. The Bureau of Internal Revenue, the stockholders, and the banks, all want special kinds of information, and generally have custom-made income statements designed to fit their requirements. Management also has peculiar demands to make of income analysis in reaching executive decisions; and the profit statement used by executives to run a business generally conforms more closely to the concepts of economic analysis than to the conventions of fiscal reporting. Many executives are unhappy about the kind of income statement produced by conventional accounting methods and feel that decision-making could be raised to a more sophisticated plane by relating income statements more closely to management's purposes.

This article attempts to examine from the managerial standpoint the major issues of profit measurement on which economists and accountants have generally taken different positions. Their most important points of difference center on: (1) the meaning of depreciation; (2) the treatment of capital gains and losses, and perhaps most important in these times (3) the price level basis for valuation of assets (i.e., current vs. historical costs).

DEPRECIATION

Treatment of depreciation is an important instance of this basic conflict. Only in the last fifty years has depreciation been a generally accepted charge against income. As businessmen came to realize that some provision must be made for the future replacement of equipment, some kind of depreciation reserve accounting was needed. The accountants' insistence that the reserve be related to the original cost rather than to the cost of replacement—which is usually quite different—gives depreciation accounting full economic usefulness only under the simplest hypothetical conditions of stable prices and foreseeable obsolescence.

The objective of depreciation in accounting is to allocate the total cost of equipment to production during the period in which it will be used. The effect is to insure that revenues equal to original cost are not distributed as dividends, but are rather put back into assets, such as more equipment or cash. Whether the amount that is thus put out of reach of dividends will actually be enough for replacement is not considered part of this accounting problem. Replacement is viewed by accountants as having no bearing on measurement of profits.

For economists, there are two distinct kinds of depreciation charge. The first is the opportunity cost of equipment, that is, the most profitable alternative use of it that is foregone by putting it to its present use. The alternative involved in using the asset for one year may be viewed as selling it at the beginning instead of the end of the year. The opportunity cost could then be measured by the fall in value of the equipment during the year. This shrinkage in disposal value, which measures the capital-wastage from postponing its disposal for one year, produces a depreciation cost estimate which is quite different from straight-line depreciation for an individual year. For example, it is common to charge as annual depreciation one-fifth of an automobile's original cost. Yet the decline in disposal value during the first year is normally nearer to 40 percent than to 20 percent of original cost. Inherently it has no relation to cost; disposal value rose during some postwar years, producing negative depreciation costs from an economic viewpoint.

The opportunity-cost of depreciation depends upon the nature of the alternative. The alternative may be to keep the equipment idle and save it for later years. Or there may be no alternative uses in other places or times, and thus no real cost of using it in its present function. A hydroelectric dam is perhaps an illustration of this kind of specialized and immobile sunk investment. The economic cost of using the equipment for one year, in any case, has nothing to do with original cost and nothing to do with eventual disposal of the equipment—the two important factors in accounting depreciation.

The second kind of depreciation cost is the exhaustion of a year's worth of limited valuable life. In the case of the dam, where there is no opportunity cost, the future useful life (which measures its unique value to the going concern) is nevertheless continually running out. To preserve owner's capital, enough of the dam's gross earnings must be saved and reinvested to shift capital out of the dam into equally profitable ventures, perhaps a replacement dam. The amount of this kind of economic depreciation is not determined by the historical cost of the equipment. It is better measured by replacement value of equipment that will produce comparable earnings. This kind of depreciation is not a cost; the cost was incurred when capital was originally frozen into the plant. Rather, it is an act of saving, and the amount to charge each year is a financial problem related to past, present, and future patterns of gross earnings, as well as to price level expectations.

Both of these economic concepts of depreciation are important to management. The first, opportunity cost, is needed for operating problems of profit-making, the second, replacement of eroded earnings ability, is needed for financial problems of preserving and administering capital. For neither, however, does original cost play any role in estimates.

TREATMENT OF CAPITAL GAINS AND LOSSES

Capital gains and losses, or "windfalls," as they are often called, may be defined loosely as unanticipated changes in the value of property relative to other real goods. That is, a windfall reflects a change in someone's anticipation of the property's earning power. Fluctuations in stock market prices are almost all of this nature.

"Property" should be interpreted broadly here to include executive ability, organizational structure, brand names, and market connections. All the assets that comprise the value of the firm are vulnerable to windfall changes. For instance, the value of cash deteriorates in inflation; accounts receivable are hit by defaults not allowed for in bad debt reserves; inventory is subject to fire, flood, price drops, and substitute competition; the value of plant facilities is slashed when competitors install new, cost-cutting equipment; and patent protection can be made worthless by a court decision. The list of possibilities is endless.

These are capital losses, which, in a progressive society, are probably larger on balance than capital gains. Many of these risks can be diluted by insurance-type charges, such as surplus reserve appropriations or high depreciation rates. And when conservative managements actually over-insure, the excess eventually appears as capital gains.

A sound accounting policy to follow concerning windfalls is to avoid recording them until they turn into cash by a purchase or sale of assets, since it is never clear until then *exactly* how large they are in dollar terms. Occasionally major write-downs are made when value has apparently been wiped out; but the chastening experience of 1929–1932 has virtually eliminated the practice of write-ups beyond original cost.

How the windfall is reported in financial statements is not a matter of interest to economists (as long as they are explained). They are concerned with the future, not the past. The important thing is that gains and losses usually can be foreseen for some time before they are realized in cash. A fact-minded management must have some sort of balance sheet, if only an estimated one that realizes surprises long before they have become exact enough to be acceptable to accountants. For example, if prices are to be determined with the objective of producing a "reasonable" rate of return on the valuation of investment, they should reflect projectable windfalls even though not yet cashed. Otherwise, a target rate of return based on an historically "factual," but nevertheless fictitious capital value, may lead to later and unpleasant surprises from the resulting price policies.

CURRENT VS. HISTORICAL COSTS

In measuring income, accountants typically state costs in terms of the price level at the time of the purchase, by recording the historical outlay, rather than in terms of the current price level. Various reasons for this have been advanced by accountants: (1) because historical costs produce more accurate measurement of income; (2) because historical costs are less debatable (more objective) than the calculation of present replacement value; (3) because the function of the accountant is to record history whether or not history has relevance for future business or economic problems, but presumably in the hope that it has.

Arguments on historical cost accounting have been going on for decades, but never was the debate more vigorous than during the 1941–1948 inflation. This was an extremely turbulent time: business was scrambling to fill postwar demand and was jockeying for new market positions; there was a rush to get new products on the market; capital expenditures were being made at a tremendous rate. The situation was rich with windfall gains and losses, resulting from the violent changes in demand, supply, and price structure. Management needed the best kind of information to keep track of conditions and to plan astutely. Inflation carried prices to nearly double their level of ten years before; a general revision of ideas was called for on the value of a dollar and the meaning of the older assets on the books. One of the significant by-products of inflation was a bitter controversy among accountants, lawyers, economists, and politicians on the truth or fiction of accounting practice in such a period. The argument was a cross-hatch of speculations on legal and moral obligations to investors, tax liabilities, established accounting traditions, future price levels, and political convenience. Out of the controversy came income statements with a rash of special reserves and footnote explanations, and some extraordinary depreciation treatments.

The implied assumption of most depreciation policies was that we would eventually get back to prewar prices. This assumption seemed quite unreal and irrelevant to most economists, and it was clear that published income statements had only begun to recognize the basic change in the purchasing power of the dollar. With prices on a new high plateau, depreciation charges in terms of prewar prices were carrying only about half the load of financing postwar replacements, and it was almost impossible to determine what part of the capital investment boom was really adding to the nation's productive capacity.

Statistics of corporate earnings were probably gross overstatements of economic earnings, although the amount of the distortion was difficult to estimate. In a period of inflation, cost of living goes up for corporations as well as for persons. The cost of refilling inventories, replacing worn equipment, and expanding capacity all go up. Yet accounting procedures generally fail to take adequate account of these increases. When inventories and depreciation are charged at original costs, rather than at the higher replacement cost, inventory and plant are revalued as they are turned over. Orthodox accounting vigilantly keeps ordinary revaluations from getting into the profit and loss account—by treating them as surplus adjustments. But when revaluations find their way into the accounts indirectly, by the process of turnover of assets during inflation, they *do* get into the earnings account. These revaluation profits are treated as ordinary business income and cannot in the books be distinguished from other income. Hence, accounting profit overstates real business income, not only during an inflation but for some time after prices have reached stability. It is clearly not enough to deflate the reported income figure by dividing money profits by some cost-of-living index after the manner in which real wages are found. Profits are a residual in a calculation that uses dollars of many different dates—today's cash dollars, last year's inventory dollars, and equipment dollars of many years of prosperity and depression. To measure real profits, all these assets must be stated in dollars of the same purchasing power. This is an elaborate operation, and the desirable data on prices, products, and dates are usually hard to estimate. With some expediting assumptions, however, usable approximations can be made.

A Note on Break-even Charts

Fortune MAGAZINE

This article appeared in the February 1949 issue of Fortune.

Essentially, the break-even chart is a graphic presentation of the relationship between revenue and expense, projected for all levels of sales. There is nothing complicated or novel about such a chart. Progressive managements have used this or similar visual aids for years. The break-even chart is no substitute for either detailed accountancy or management judgment.

The basic chart (Chart 1) was developed some forty years ago by Professor Walter Rautenstrauch of the Industrial Engineering Department of Columbia University. It is the great granddaddy of the many sales-profit charts in use today, and is, in some respects, superior to them. The 45-degree sales line makes it possible to plot the break-even points for any number of years or months on a single chart, and to compare charts for different companies, products, etc. A prerequisite to the construction of this or any other break-even chart, however, is a knowledge of which business expenses are constant and which are variable with changes in volume. Once that is known a total-expense line can be drawn for all levels of sales. Few firms customarily break down their costs in this manner, however. Take, for example, the remuneration paid a salesman. Normal accountancy would probably lump his commissions, salary, and bonus together as sales expense. Actually, however, his commission is a variable

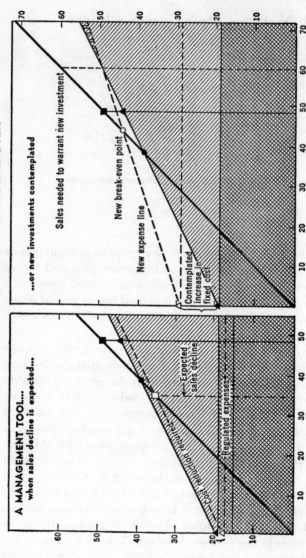

CHART 1 FINDING XYZ COMPANY'S BREAK-EVEN POINT

The construction of a break-even chart involves three simple steps. Step 1: Expenses that vary directly with volume (materials, sales commissions, etc.) are segregated from constant expenses (real-estate taxes, depreciation, interest, etc.). Step 2: The total expense line is then plotted on a grid with identical horizontal and vertical dollar scales. Step 3: A sales line is superimposed on this grid forming a 45-degree angle with both scales. That this method of plotting the break-even point is accurate is attested by the fact that the computed break-even volume for the company above (an actual firm) was $38.4 million.

CHART 2

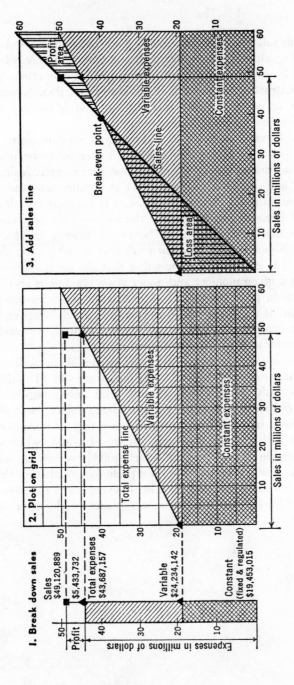

I. Break down sales

Sales $49,120,889

Profit $5,433,732

Total expenses $43,687,157

Variable $24,234,142

Constant (fixed & regulated) $19,453,015

Expenses in millions of dollars

2. Plot on grid

Total expense line

Variable expenses

Constant expenses

Sales in millions of dollars

3. Add sales line

Break-even point

Sales line

Variable expenses

Constant expenses

Profit area

Loss area

Sales in millions of dollars

The hypothetical cases above illustrate two of the many ways a break-even chart can be used in management planning. If sales decline $15 million (left) a $4-million loss will result unless costs are cut. If, on the other hand, an investment is contemplated that will increase constant expense by $10 million (right) it can be seen that sales of $60 million are needed to justify the new expense structure.

expense, his salary a constant expense, and his bonus a regulated expense; i.e., although constant in that it is not directly related to sales, it is nevertheless subject to management discretion. The trick of constructing an accurate break-even chart, then, is largely dependent upon proper cost analysis, but that is equally true when the break-even point is computed.

The break-even chart is like a household tape measure. It has many practical uses and yet does not pretend to be microscopically accurate. The total-expense line, for example, is simply a straight line drawn from fixed costs at volume zero through total cost at current volume. No attempt is made at curvilinear refinement because cost figures are themselves mere approximations. Nor can valid deductions be drawn from a break-even chart at volumes widely different from that on which the chart is based. It is important to remember that the chart represents expense at a given moment and under given conditions and that any change in price, wages, *et al.*, will alter the sales-expense relationship. If these limitations are borne in mind, however, the break-even chart can be used to analyze and control costs and to estimate profits under a variety of assumptions.

In Chart 2, the effect of a sales decline or of an additional capital outlay are considered. A decline in sales of $15 million would obviously put the firm into the red unless regulatable expenses (research, promotion, the president's salary, etc.) were cut $4 million. In the other case it is assumed that a contemplated investment will increase constant cost by $10 million but will reduce variable expenses. The chart quickly shows at what volume the new investment becomes profitable. Although these charts are for an entire company, break-even charts can also be constructed for individual departments, plants, products, or even salesmen.

The Importance of the Price Elasticity of Demand

*Edwin Mansfield is Professor of Economics
at the Wharton School, University of Pennsylvania. This article was written for the
present volume.*

The price elasticity of demand is the percentage change in the quantity demanded that results from a 1 percent increase in price. A sharp distinction should be made between an industry's elasticity and a particular firm's elasticity. Whereas the former gauges the sensitivity of total industry demand to industry-wide changes in price, the latter shows the sensitivity of demand for a particular firm's product to changes in its price, the price set by other firms in the industry being held constant. A firm's elasticity depends heavily on the similarity of its product to that of competitors. For instance, a Gulf station is likely to lose a considerable share of its market to a neighboring Esso station whose price is half a cent a gallon less.

The price elasticity of demand is of great importance to the firm. When costs are increasing, it is tempting for the firm to pass on the increases by raising the price to the consumer. If demand for the product is relatively inelastic,[1] this action may succeed.

1. Demand at a particular price is said to be inelastic if the price elasticity is less than one in absolute value. In this case, total revenue decreases with decreases in price.

However, when there are many substitutes and demand is quite elastic,[2] increasing prices may lead to a reduction in total revenues rather than an increase. The result may be lower rather than higher profits. Similarly, businessmen are sometimes surprised by a lack of success of price reductions, this merely being a reflection of the fact that demand is relatively inelastic.

Most businessmen intuitively are aware of the elasticity of demand of the goods they make, although they may not have a detailed, precise estimate. Nonetheless, some firms tend to be conservative and underestimate the elasticity of demand. For example, classical phonograph records were high-priced luxury items for a long time. In 1938, Columbia cut the price per record from $2 to $1, and the response was overwhelming. To the surprise of much of the industry, total expenditure on classical records rose greatly, the price elasticity of demand being relatively large.

Using techniques like those described in "Estimating the Price Elasticity of Demand," it is possible to estimate the price elasticity of demand for a particular product. Some of the results are shown in Table 1. As would be expected, the price elasticity of demand for basic foodstuffs is relatively low. For sugar, potatoes, hay, and wheat, it is less than 0.5 percent in absolute value. That is, a 1 percent increase in the price of these products will result in less than a 0.5 percent decrease in the quantity consumed. On the other hand, the demand for millinery is quite elastic, a 1 percent increase in price leading to a 3 percent decrease in quantity consumed.

One of the most important factors influencing the price elasticity of demand is the availability of substitutes. If a product is faced with extremely close substitutes, its demand will be very elastic. For example, take the case of the Gulf and Esso dealers cited above. Their products, location, and services are so similar that a very small differential in price will result in a considerable shift in sales. On the other hand, in the case of basic foodstuffs such close substitutes do not exist, the result being that the price elasticity of demand is much lower.

2. Demand at a particular price is said to be elastic if the price elasticity is greater than one in absolute value, in which case total revenue increases with decreases in price.

TABLE 1

ESTIMATED PRICE ELASTICITIES OF DEMAND FOR SELECTED
COMMODITIES, UNITED STATES

Product	Price elasticity
beef	—0.92
millinery	—3.00
gasoline	—0.52
sugar	—0.31
corn	—0.49
cotton	—0.12
hay	—0.43
wheat	—0.08
potatoes	—0.31
oats	—0.56
barley	—0.39
buckwheat	—0.99

Source: H. Schultz, *Theory and Measurement of Demand* (Chicago: University of Chicago Press, 1938), and M. Spencer and L. Siegelman, *Managerial Economics* (Homewood, Ill.: Richard D. Irwin, 1959).

Finally, to illustrate very briefly the sorts of studies that have been made of the price elasticity of demand, consider a study of the fare structure of the New York subway and its effect on passenger travel. Table 2 gives forecasts of demand and revenues

TABLE 2

ALTERNATIVE ESTIMATES OF DEMAND CURVE FOR SUBWAY
SERVICE

(passengers and revenues in millions per year)

	Case A		Case B		Case C		Case D	
Fare (cents)	Passengers	Revenues	Passengers	Revenues	Passengers	Revenues	Passengers	Revenues
5	1945	$97.2	1945	$97.2	1945	$97.2	1945	$97.2
10	1683	168.3	1683	168.3	1683	168.3	1683	168.3
15	1421	213.2	1458	218.7	1530	229.5	1547	232.0
20	1159	231.8	1262	252.4	1421	284.2	1457	291.5
25	897	224.2	1092	273.0	1347	336.8	1390	348.2
30	635	190.5	945	283.5	1278	383.4	1340	402.0

Source: W. S. Vickrey, *The Revision of the Rapid Transit Fare Structure of the City of New York* (Technical Monograph No. 3, Finance Project, Mayor's Committee on Management Survey of the City of New York), p. 87.

based on various fare levels. In Case *A*, quantity demanded was
a linear function of price, i.e.,

$$q = a - bp$$

where q is quantity demanded and p is price. In Case *B*,

$$\log q = a - bp.$$

In Case *C*,

$$q = a - b \log p.$$

And in Case *D*,

$$\log q = a - b \log p.$$

The author concludes that Case *B* probably represents the most
reasonable case. We are not concerned here with the methods
used to derive such estimates or with the factors that prompted
him to choose Case *B* over the others. Methods of estimation
are discussed in the subsequent paper. For present purposes,
the important thing is the relevance of the information provided
in Table 2 to decisions that must be made by the firm. Table 2
shows that the demand for this product is inelastic—and the
extent to which it is inelastic. In determining its price policy,
the New York Transit Authority would do well to recognize this
fact. Although price reductions for some items, like Columbia's
records, may be profitable, in this case they will reduce both
revenues and profits.

Estimating the Price Elasticity
of Demand

JOEL DEAN

*Joel Dean is Professor of Business Economics
at Columbia University's Graduate School of
Business. This article comes from his book,*
Managerial Economics, *published in 1960.*

CONTROLLED EXPERIMENTS

The most promising method of estimating short-run price
elasticity for the product of an individual firm is usually by
controlled experiments. The essence of this method is to vary
separately certain determinants of demand which can be manipulated, e.g., prices, advertising, packaging, and try to conduct the
experiment so that other market conditions either remain fairly
constant or can be allowed for. Geographic differentiation is one
way to manipulate prices or marketing strategy, comparing sales
in separate localities, and usually reversing the arrangement as
a check to eliminate the effects of other factors. Or prices and
promotion can be manipulated through time in the same market,
although this is usually less informative.

The Parker Pen Co. conducted a price experiment recently to
determine whether they should raise the price of Quink, which
was then selling at a loss to the company and at little profit to
the dealer. The increase in price from 15¢ to 25¢ was tested in
four cities. Results indicated such low elasticity of demand that

the sales loss was more than offset by the added profit margin. After the price was advanced, experimentation was continued in cooperation with fifty dealers. In some stores the old package priced at 15¢ was placed next to a package marked "New Quink, 25¢." Two out of five customers bought the 25¢ package. In other stores Quink was placed on display beside competitive inks priced at 15¢ and at 10¢. In order to test specifically cross-elasticity of demand Quink was sold at 15¢ for two weeks, then at 25¢ for another two weeks. At the higher price there was a slight decline of Quink sales in relation to sales of two competitive inks. Consumer panel reports indicated that volume declined at first and then began to rise both absolutely and relative to competitors. Several competitors followed the price advance of Parker, which is the largest ink manufacturer.

Another example of field tests of competitive cross-elasticity is the Simmons Mattress experiment. Identical mattresses, some bearing the Simmons brand and others an unknown brand, were offered for sale, first at the same prices and then at various price-spreads, to determine the effect on sales. With parity prices the Simmons brand outsold the other fifteen to one; with a five dollar premium, sales were eight to one; and with a 25 percent premium, sales were equal. A parallel experiment with Cannon towels produced similar results.

Field testing of prices is sometimes used in connection with the introduction of new products. Thus, a manufacturer of duplicating supplies introduced a new product in two supposedly comparable geographic areas at different prices. The indicated demand elasticity was less than unity so the product was priced at the higher level. A similar case is that of a large food manufacturer who was faced with the problem of setting the price for frozen orange juice when it was first introduced. He experimented with three different prices in different cities. All three prices were below the then parity level of fresh oranges. Sales did not appear to differ significantly among the three price levels.

To cite another example, a new type of roll-around shopping cart which collapses into an eminently portable form was developed recently. Experimental probing for the right price included an effort to sell it house-to-house for $4.98. But it wouldn't go. Simultaneously, a large Chicago department store was supplied with a lot to be offered at $3.98. At this price and through this channel the shopping carts sold well. Efforts to pare the costs enough to make it profitable to sell at this price through department stores were unsuccessful, however, so the product had to be withdrawn from the market.

For products that are normally sold by mail order, opportunities for experimental analysis of demand are rich. Price, promotion, and even product design, can be varied among keyed mailings, chosen as successive samples of the same prospect population. Several years ago a mail-order house sent out a batch of catalogs in which the price of one item varied from $1.88 to $1.99 and then observed the relation of sales to the range of prices to find the price elasticity.

A new product that is not to be permanently sold by mail can be experimentally offered by direct mail at different prices to carefully controlled and geographically separated sectors of a mailing list. By analyzing the actual order response to each of the series of prices, some conception of demand elasticity can be obtained. This approach may be viewed as a variant of the prospect questionnaire method, but it avoids the difficulty of bridging the gap between declaration of intention and actual purchasing action. It has limitations both in the difficulty of getting satisfactory comparability of the market sectors and in the failure to duplicate the actual purchasing environment.

There are serious problems in determining demand schedules by controlled experiments. Such experiments are expensive, hazardous and time-consuming. In planning the study it is not always clear just what conditions should be held constant. Moreover, it is difficult, costly, and dangerous to set up a pricing experiment that will include all the effects of a price change that you want to measure, and exclude all the effects of other factors that you don't want. It is hard to reflect realistically the reaction of rivals to the price change. And dealers' responses are often atypical since they are privy to the experiment. The temporary impact of a local price raid may be all that is measured, whereas the problem concerns the effect of full-scale and more permanent price reductions. For example, the great responsiveness of sales to price-cuts in the Macy experiment conducted by Whitman (discussed below) probably measures stocking-up to take advantage of a short-lived opportunity and also reflects lags by competitors in meeting Macy's prices. Sufficient reaction time to feel the full effect of price is seldom possible before other conditions change significantly. Thus, the results often have limited generality, since they are tied to the particular conditions of the experiment.

Pricing experiments are costly and hazardous. They run risks of unfavorable side-reactions of dealers, consumers, and competitors. Nonetheless, this method deserves wider use than it has had, and constitutes one of the most promising implements for demand analysis in current markets.

CONSUMER QUESTIONNAIRES

Personal interviews and written questionnaires are widely used to probe the buying motives, intentions and habits of customers and prospects. They are sometimes helpful (in the absence of better measurements) in guessing at the sensitivity of demand to price. Little confidence can be placed in answers to questions that ask consumers what they think they would pay, or how much they would buy if prices were lower, or if price-spreads over competitors and substitutes were different. This kind of frontal attack on the intricate psychological problem of buyers' intentions and actions is still a highly dubious method of analysis, even when the market consists of a few large industrial customers. Not until the psychometric techniques of depth interviewing have advanced far beyond their present status can much be expected from such direct probing.

But collateral information obtained from such interviews can brace up a guess at price sensitivity. For example, interviews revealed that most buyers of a branded baby food chose it on their doctor's recommendation, and that most were quite ignorant about substitutes and about prices. This knowledge, together with other information, led the manufacturer to guess that demand for his product was quite inelastic.

Occasionally questionnaire research can indicate the outer limits of price. For example, an automatic timer developed for photographers was never commercialized because questionnaires indicated that the lowest profitable price was far above what most photographers *said* they would pay. But in general such research is a frail foundation for pricing decisions.

ENGINEERING ESTIMATES

For producers' goods, it is sometimes possible to guess at the effect of price upon the sales of a capital good by making engineering estimates of the cost savings and other benefits that can be produced by the product for a sample of prospects. By applying some standard of capital earnings, e.g., a three-year crude pay-out, it is possible to translate estimates of savings into demand for equipment.

The cost savings of customers will vary because prospects differ in size, wage rate, efficiency of displaced equipment, and other such conditions. To estimate the way these divergent conditions affect the quantity of equipment that will be purchased, a sample of prospects that is representative of various strata of customer size, wage rates, equipment efficiency, etc., is selected. From estimates of the cost savings and the number of prospects in each category, the sample results can be blown up to yield a projected schedule of equipment sales at various prices. Estimates of the cost savings of new equipment types can be supplemented and verified by test installations in major prospect categories.

The most difficult practical problems usually arise not in estimating the cost savings in a particular situation, but in translating these savings into a demand schedule that reflects a composite of all situations. Comprehensive knowledge of the operations of a buying industry are required for the equipment, both to determine the appropriate conversion factors for capitalizing cost savings and to select the sample and blow it up.[1]

1. This approach concentrates on obsolescence replacement, since it is here that pricing affects engineering feasibility. Cultural lags of ignorance, uncertainty, and speculation contaminate this relationship. Buying equipment on the basis of its prospective earnings on capital is unfortunately not yet sufficiently common to be the sole basis for analysis of demand. The age, distribution, and the status of depreciation reserves of existing equipment, though they should be irrelevant, may properly enter into forecasts of the rate of displacement of obsolete machinery.

CORRELATION ANALYSIS

Often, information on price elasticity can be found by applying a correlation technique to historical records of prices and sales. The important problem in this method is to design a function that can sift out the price relations from data that show the composite effect of all sales determinants.

Correlation analysis of price elasticity has been applied most extensively to demand for agricultural products, notably by Henry Schultz. Using very simple relationships[2] Schultz found fairly high correlations of price and consumption for most farm products[3] over periods of about fifteen years.

Farm products have economic characteristics that make them particularly susceptible to this kind of analysis: they are homogeneous and staple, so that their demand curves change very slowly over the years; they are sold in highly competitive markets, where prices are flexibly adjusted to demand and supply; supply varies widely from year to year, but annual production, once under way, is hard to control by producers. Wide swings in supply plus highly stable demand can in these conditions be assumed to produce a series of prices that, when plotted against consumption, trace out the shape of the demand curve.

These are far different pricing conditions from those prevailing in manufacturing industry, where prices are a combination of rigid, official quotations and undercover concessions, where products are rarely comparable, and where current demand is more closely matched by current production. Nevertheless, in some industries, price data for this kind of analysis is produced inadvertently. Price wars, regional differences in competitive

2. For instance, he used functions in the forms

$$x = a + by + ct$$
$$x = Ay^m e^{nt}$$

where x is per capita consumption, y is the deflated price, and t is time, while $a,b,c,A,m,n,$ and e are constants. In another form of analysis, price and consumption were used not in absolute terms but as deviations from a long-term trend; time was omitted as an explicit variable. Another variant of the analysis was a correlation of year-to-year changes in price with corresponding changes in consumption, a method first used by Henry Moore (*Economic Cycles: Their Law and Cause,* New York, 1914).

3. An important exception was wheat, for which price behavior was largely governed by a world market rather than a national one.

and substitute price spreads, and the distortion of relative prices caused by inflation create research opportunities that are too often neglected. Statistical analysis of such price experience can sometimes provide usable knowledge about how prices and price spreads affect both the company's market share and the industry's battle with substitutes. A state sales tax on soft drinks recently created data inadvertently that demonstrated a high price elasticity for one bottling company. This company found that a one cent per bottle tax could not be added to the wholesale price without cutting volume enough to lower total revenue. Differences in state taxes on gasoline, together with geographical differences in laid-down cost, have furnished oil companies with data for making correlation analyses of the relationships between price and volume.

When a product's price is rigid, changes in substitutes' prices shift the relative price of the product and give data on price elasticity. For example, in studying the price elasticity of policy-loans made by an insurance company, it was found that the policy-loan rate stayed constant while competing lenders reduced their rates. Thus the relative price of policy-loans was rising in a way that was measurable and could be related to changes in loan volume, both absolutely and relative to competitors' volume.

PRICE ELASTICITY—AN ILLUSTRATIVE STUDY

One of the best studies of the short-run relation of price to sales was done for Macy's department store by R. H. Whitman.[4] In several respects this is an ideal field for such research: (1) prices are an important sales factor—they are featured in advertising, and customers shop between stores; (2) prices are unusually flexible—seasonal patterns and style cycles make careful price administration a must for managing large inventories profitably; (3) there is substantial and regular competition among stores, but with some leeway for price policy; (4) there is keen competition between substitute products on the same counter, which presents the raw material for well controlled experiments.

4. "Demand Functions for Merchandise at Retail," *Studies in Mathematical Economics and Econometrics* (Chicago: University of Chicago Press, 1942), pp. 208-221.

Whitman was thus able to sidestep some of the obstacles discussed earlier in the chapter. For instance, he used a very short time period (two and one-half months), which stabilized consumer income, but which nevertheless saw many price changes. He analyzed only staple products in order to obviate the style cycles problem. He assumed that when Macy's changed its price the pattern of reactions of other stores during the analysis period would be repeated under similar conditions in the future. These simplifying circumstances neutralized the effect of several independent variables that must be used in most demand situations, and permitted him to use simple correlation of price and quantity sold to find price elasticity.

Whitman created his data by systematically manipulating price over a wide range during a short period. Parallel experiments were performed for a number of staples.

When correlation analysis is worked out in its mathematical (least-squares) form, the first step is to set up an algebraic function to express the relation. There is usually room for judgment in deciding on the best form to use. In choosing his demand equation, Whitman rejected the common form, $q = a + bp$ and used instead $q = Ap^a$. ($q =$ quantity sold; $p =$ price; A, a, and b are constants.)[5]

CHART 1

ALTERNATIVE FORMS OF DEMAND FUNCTION

5. Exponential functions of this type are used in logarithmic form for correlation analysis:

$$\log q = \log A + a \log p.$$

An important feature of the hyperbolic demand curve is its constant elasticity: regardless of the level of price, the ratio of a small fixed percent change in price to the resulting percent change in quantity sold is constant. This ratio is equal to the constant a, which is the price elasticity of demand, and which is negative. For example, if a is -5, a drop in price of 1 percent will increase sales by 5 percent and revenue by 4 percent. In the simplest case, where $a = -1$, sales vary inversely with price just enough to keep total revenue constant for all values of p.

In the straight-line demand curve, on the other hand, a \$1 change in price will produce a constant absolute change in quantity sold regardless of the level of price. In this case there is a price which gives a maximum revenue, namely $a/2$.

Whether the hyperbola is more realistic is not clear *a priori:* there is certainly a price where none at all can be sold, and the amount that can be given away is also finite. But for the relevant range of actual prices, Whitman found it a better fit to the facts than a straight line.

The price elasticities that resulted from this analysis told a significant story and were surprisingly reliable in a statistical sense. Chart 1 presents the demand schedule for one product, showing a price elasticity of about -6 (with a standard error of .78) and a correlation coefficient of $-.89$, which indicates a close relation between sales and prices. Other commodities showed comparable price elasticities and correlations. Moreover, by comparing results for the same calendar months in two successive years, Whitman found that the change during the year was relatively slight compared to the margin of probable error.

These price elasticities are relatively high, and mean that sales are sensitive to prices for these products. For these products, price is a powerful weapon in competition—probably too powerful to be used freely. Low elasticity, in contrast, shows products where price competition is too ineffective to be important, compared to the returns from advertising.

Whitman also ran a multiple correlation analysis to find the relation of sales to prices of other products, using as independent variables both the product's price and an index of competing

CHART 2

DEPARTMENT STORE DEMAND FUNCTION

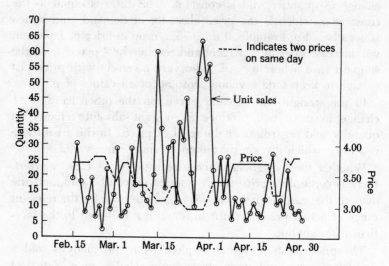

(Source: R. H. Whitman, "Demand Functions for Merchandise at Retail," *Studies in Mathematical Economics and Econometrics,* Chicago, University of Chicago Press, 1942, pp. 210, 214.)

CHART 3

DEPARTMENT STORE PRICES AND SALES. ORIGINAL DATA

(Source: R. H. Whitman, "Demand Functions for Merchandise at Retail," *Studies in Mathematical Economics and Econometrics,* Chicago, University of Chicago Press, 1942, pp. 210, 214.)

products.[6] The closeness of fit for this equation was not impressively high, but the analysis did contribute some information on cross elasticity of demand, which for different products ranged from 1.4 to 16.2.

As we indicated above, this analysis had a rather ideal short-run setting, which is unattainable for most products. It is much more common for prices to change from year to year than from day to day, and for reaction patterns to be much slower. Nevertheless, it is highly probable that there are other areas where it can be useful.

6. The equation took the form: $Q = Ap^a P^b$.

Pricing and the Character of
the Product

A. D. H. KAPLAN, JOEL B. DIRLAM,
AND ROBERT F. LANZILLOTTI

*A. D. H. Kaplan is a senior economist at the
Brookings Institution. Together with Joel
Dirlam and Robert Lanzillotti, he wrote*
Pricing in Big Business *from which the fol-
lowing paper is taken.*

The character of the product—the type of demand to which it
caters, as well as its physical attributes, production requirements,
amenability to differentiation, and stage of maturity—sets boundaries to the pricing discretion of the company, big or little. When
interpreting the role of product characteristics, however, the
possibility that reaction may run both ways must be kept in mind.
These characteristics are not fixed or unadjustable. They themselves may be affected by price. But the basic concern at this
point is with pricing policies that seem to be imposed by the
nature of the product, rather than vice versa.

With a product like fresh meat, perishable and subject to unpredictable output and shipments of the primary commodity, even a
firm of the importance of Swift & Company has a limited opportunity to bend wholesale prices to company policy. A durable
product with controlled raw material output, and production
based on orders, better lends itself to fairly stable price quotations, as in steel or crude oil. Copper, on the contrary, with its

volatile price behavior points up the effect on the manageability of prices of a widely diffused raw material supply and a world market. Limitations on the transportability of the product (transportation cost in relation to product value) may give locational advantage in pricing even when there are business giants in the industry.

New products, with varying degrees of marketable uniqueness, provide opportunities for pricing discretion not generally available in standardized goods. Large companies whose resources are concentrated in established standard products are aware of the general unprofitability of price wars when confronted with similarly large and resourceful competitors; hence they keep in step with the competition on price and depend on such factors as favorable location, or availability of adequate supplies and satisfactory service to customers, for their competitive strength at the going price. In the use of these devices, however, product features (*e.g.*, vulnerability to substitution) may determine how successful a stable price policy can be, even for the large and resourceful company.

New Products and Matured Products · The natural frame of reference for pricing a new product is the price range of existing substitutes. For example, it was recognized that nylon was capable of penetrating the markets of a variety of textile fibers. The problem of effectively introducing this new fiber resolved itself through a compromise between pricing for the widest possible use and pricing for the more limited, but in the long run, more sustainable and profitable quality market. In cellophane, the same company reached more aggressively for more extensive market penetration without undermining the profit potential. Apparently, the cost elasticity of volume output and the price elasticity of growing demand were sufficiently high to permit a more rapid rate of expansion than was possible in nylon. The introduction of a major consumer appliance, for which demand is as yet an expectation rather than a reality, has entailed elaborate market research to select a price niche that will permit the inclusion of features required for optimum acceptance. In the pricing of a major piece of farm machinery such as the cotton picker, the decision settles on a middle ground between the estimated maxi-

mum economic value as a replacement for hand labor and a
sufficiently low price to give assurance of widespread adoption.
Prices determined in this manner may well limit the components
that can be selected for incorporation in the assembled product;
automobiles and other consumer durables considered earlier were
cases in point. With the accumulation of know-how and the
lowering of costs, subsequent pricing turns on whether the
product can readily be imitated, whether the prestige acquired
in its pioneering can be prolonged through improvement and
product differentiation, or whether lower cost reflected in lower
price will open up a highly profitable volume increase.

An established standard product, be it a metal, flour, or heavy
chemical, does not entail such conscious balancing of alternative
possibilities to fix its price levels. The price may start from a
fairly well-recognized cost base, but the profit is a residual reflect-
ing the current willingness or ability of the market to keep the
capacity employed. Large firms with heavy investments in established areas of primary production have constantly feared that
price changes will lead to hazards of unpredictable magnitude.
This fear has often been justified in the past—witness the gyra-
tions of price with accompanying demand fluctuations in copper,
lead, or zinc; and even with price leadership, boom and depression fluctuations in steel prices have not been unknown. There
is in consequence an undercurrent of antipathy in the firms inter-
viewed to policies that would disturb the pattern of stable and
infrequently changing prices. The instability of copper prices is
certainy not due to lack of desire on the part of Kennecott and
other primary producers to keep firm the price of their metal.
The volatility issues rather from the fickleness of a world market,
in which fluctuation is accentuated by extremes of overflow or
scarcity in the supply of copper scrap.

At least until the Second World War, Alcoa supplied and
priced aluminum in the United States with some regard to the
fact that it had to penetrate the markets of copper and other
metals as well as some non-metallic products. Its technical development in a capital-intensive form with integrated production
and standardization of finished products now tends to assert itself;
so that while product promotion remains vigorous, pricing in the

basic aluminum lines is showing resemblances to steel's pattern of base prices and extras.

The type of use to which a product is put also has a bearing on the importance attached to price variations. The stable pricing of containers carried by American Can and Continental Can has met with little resistance by their customers, and this is not solely because of the duopoly leadership in can manufacture; it is largely due to the fact that what the final user is buying is not the container but the contents. Similarly, flexible packaging materials, aluminum fabrications, special electrical equipment items, and industrial gases permit the manufacturer a minimum of concern with price competition because these are products sold as part—an incidental part—of the larger end product in which the cost of the contributing item is not a prime consideration.

Cost Structure · Production and cost characteristics of the main product play a primary role in conditioning pricing policies. The overriding importance of certain materials in the total cost structure, as in the case of tin plate for can manufacture; the leanness of the ore, and the consequent magnitude of the mining operations of Kennecott Copper; the relatively small runs and large number of items, as in the case of Alcoa's fabricated operations; and of course the high proportion of indirect cost in basic steel production—all these distinctive features are transmuted into pricing policy. U. S. Steel seeks to avoid cutthroat price competition, and evolves a fair return philosophy. Alcoa finds a standard cost system unusable for many items. Kennecott, when prices drop, has to pile up inventory and await more settled prices; it looks with favor on stabilized prices. American Can, and perhaps even the oil companies, in the long run, become transmission belts for passing material and labor costs on to consumers with an inelastic demand. Thus a large part of price policy may be the response to the cost pattern inherent to the product.

Time Adjustments of Flows of Funds

PEARSON HUNT,
CHARLES M. WILLIAMS, AND
GORDON DONALDSON

Pearson Hunt is Professor of Business Administration at Harvard University. In 1961, together with Charles Williams and Gordon Donaldson, he published Basic Business Finance *from which this paper is taken.*

Many decisions involve in some way a comparison of the usefulness of receiving or paying funds at one time rather than another, and we need a means of evaluating the effect of the time span involved. The procedure of *time adjustment* provides a consistent and accurate means for the needed evaluation.

One basic assumption must be made before application of the mathematical procedure, which involves nothing more than compound interest. We assume that a firm always can find some way to invest funds to produce some net gain, or *rate of return*. The rate may be very low, as when funds are temporarily placed in short-term treasury bills, or it may be as high as the gain from some new product greatly in demand. In fact, if a firm does not act to obtain some return from the use of its funds, we speak of the *opportunity cost*, which is the loss of revenue because an opportunity was not taken. Therefore, since there can always be earnings from the investment of funds, we can say as a general rule that whenever a business has a choice of the time when it will obtain certain funds, the rule should be "the sooner, the better."

The first step to an understanding of time adjustment is to relate the amounts involved to one another along a scale of time. The time is divided into periods (e.g., days, months, years), and a particular point in time is selected as the starting point from which the effect of compound interest on the funds will be regarded. This time is named the *focal date*. Periods later than this date are designated by the plus sign, periods earlier by the minus sign, and the focal date is designated by zero. To the mathematician, it is unimportant what actual time is chosen as the focal date. The financial analyst can choose any date, past or present, most convenient for his purposes. In fact, for many problems of financial planning, it is convenient to have the focal date in the future, usually the date at which a specific sum will be received or paid, or at which a certain periodic flow of funds will terminate.

It is necessary to calculate the changing values of flows of funds as they occur both before and after the focal date. We first turn to *compounding*, that is, the subsequent growth in the value of funds initially invested at the focal date, because this process is one with which most readers will be familiar from such well-advertised operations as savings accounts on which interest is compounded. We shall then turn to *discounting*, which looks in the other direction from the focal date along the time scale.

COMPOUNDING

There are three quantities necessary for the calculation:

1. *The rate of return.* In the following exposition, to show the effects of different rates, we shall use two that are well within the range of business experience.
2. *The amount of funds in question.* It is convenient to use the sum of $1.00 to develop the formulas, since if one knows how the values of this sum are affected by time, one can compute the values of any other sum by simple multiplication.
3. *The length of time from the focal date.* This may be measured in days, weeks, etc., so that for the sake of generality,

one refers to the *period* rather than to some specific unit of time. One warning is necessary here. The rate of return used must be stated consistently with the actual length of the time period. Thus, 6 percent per year becomes 0.5 percent per month, and so on.

The growing amount that will be found at later times from an investment of $1.00 at the focal date is referred to as the *compound amount* (of a single sum). Interest is computed on the original sum and then added to the original sum at the end of the first period. The new and larger principal is then the base for the interest calculation in the second period, and so on. Jumping over the detailed mathematics, we can turn to any set of tables for business computations, among which we shall find values for the compound amount of a single sum invested at a given time. See Table 1 for a portion of such a table.

DISCOUNTING

The process of compounding discloses how the value of an investment made at the focal date grows in later time. We now turn to *discounting*, a process which looks at times preceding the focal date and answers the question: How much must be invested before the focal date to produce a desired sum at the time of the focal date?

The answers to such questions are determined by using the reciprocals of the values in the table of compound amounts, for the reasons exemplified in the following instance. Take four periods and 4 percent. Table 1 shows that if $1.00 is compounded

TABLE 1

COMPOUND AMOUNT OF $1.00

Periods	Rate 4%	Rate 10%
0	1.000	1.000
+1	1.040	1.100
+2	1.082	1.210
+3	1.125	1.331
+4	1.170	1.464
+5	1.217	1.611

for this time and rate, it will increase to $1.17. To have only $1.00 at the end of four periods of compounding, we obviously need to invest less than $1.00. The calculation is:

$$\frac{1.000}{1.170} = \frac{x}{1.000}$$

$$x = 0.855$$

The number so produced is known as the *present value* (at the selected time and rate) which will produce $1.00 at the focal date. The term *discounted value* is also used, although less frequently.

Since present values are often used in financial calculations, a table of present values is provided in most books on finance. For convenience, we reproduce a portion of such a table in Table 2.

Having shown how to evaluate a sum both before the focal date (by discounting) and after the focal date (by compounding), we are in a position to picture the changing value of the sum of $1.00 at the time of the focal date over a time scale. This is presented graphically in Chart 1, where the figures from Tables 1 and 2 are used.

The basic relationships to be observed are simple but very important:

1. The value of a sum invested at any time grows as time passes.
2. The necessary investment to produce a future sum decreases as the time to produce it is increased.
3. Both these effects are magnified as the rate of return increases.

TABLE 2

PRESENT VALUE OF $1.00

Periods	Rate 4%	Rate 10%
0	1.000	1.000
−1	0.962	0.909
−2	0.925	0.826
−3	0.889	0.751
−4	0.855	0.683
−5	0.822	0.621

CHART 1

Effects of Time Adjustment: Single Sum

at 10%

at 4%

	Values	

at 4%	0.822	0.855	0.889	0.925	0.962	1.000	1.040	1.082	1.125	1.170	1.217
at 10%	0.621	0.683	0.751	0.826	0.909	1.000	1.100	1.210	1.331	1.464	1.611
	−5	−4	−3	−2	−1	0	+1	+2	+3	+4	+5

Earlier:
Present values or
discounted values

Focal date

Later:
Future values or
compound amounts

Time scale

EXAMPLES OF COMPOUNDING AND DISCOUNTING

We shall now present two simple examples of how problems of compounding and discounting arise in business, and briefly indicate the nature of their solution.

Example 1. A firm with a major debt maturity at the end of two years sets aside $500,000 for investment in tax-exempt bonds at 4 percent to help meet the maturity. How much will be available from this source when the debt matures?

The problem is one of compounding. The focal date is the present, and the period is two years. From Table 1, we find 1.082 as the compound amount of $1.00 at 4 percent. Multiplying by $500,000 gives us $541,000, which is the sum that will be on hand.

Example 2. A factor often given importance when a firm is deciding whether to own or lease land and buildings is the residual value of the property that the firm would own if it bought rather than leased. Suppose that a certain property, now costing $1 million, is expected to be worth $2 million after allowance for taxes on the capital gain at the end of twenty-five years. How much importance should this terminal value have on a decision now?

The problem is one of discounting. The concept of opportunity cost also enters. Let us assume that the firm averages 10 percent return (after taxes) on assets invested in the business. One way to obtain $2 million at the end of twenty-five years is by holding the real estate. An alternative way would be to invest some funds now and use them at 10 percent to produce $2 million. What present investment at 10 percent will produce $2 million at a focal date twenty-five years hence? From Table 2 we find that the present value of $1.00 at 10 percent after twenty-five periods is 0.092. Multiplying by $2 million, we obtain $184,000. Thus, the desired value can be obtained either by using $184,000 in the business, allowing profits to compound, or by spending $1 million to buy the property. The possibility of error in overvaluing the expectation of remote capital gains is shown by this example. It is particularly serious when high rates of return are available from funds used otherwise in the business.

FINDING THE RATE OF RETURN

There is another use to which tables of present values are often put in financial work. Given values at two dates, one is sometimes required to find the rate of return that will produce a desired change in value. Using the figures from Example 2 above, the problem can be stated as follows: At what rate of return will $1 million grow to $2 million in twenty-five years?

The focal date is the end of the twenty-five-year period, when the present value table expects $1.00 to be paid. Converting the data from the actual case therefore requires division of the initial and terminal value by $2 million:

$$\frac{2,000,000}{2,000,000} = 1.000$$

and

$$\frac{1,000,000}{2,000,000} = 0.500.$$

The question has become: At what rate of discount will 0.50 become 1.00 at the end of twenty-five periods?

Looking at a table of present values for twenty-five periods, we find:

Rate 2%......................0.610
Rate 4%......................0.375

By the process of interpolation,[1] we find the answer, which is 2.9 percent (much lower—and therefore less desirable—than the use of funds to produce 10 percent).

ANNUITIES

Our explanation of the effects of time on the value of funds has so far dealt only with single sums. That is, we have confined ourselves to watching the growth in value of a single in-

1. $2\% = 0.610$ $2\% = 0.610$
   $\underline{4\% = 0.375}$ $\underline{x = 0.500}$ $\dfrac{110}{235}$ $(2\%) = x = 0.9\%$
   $2\% = 0.235$ 0.110

vestment, once it is made. We now turn to what is perhaps more frequently experienced in business, namely, the receipt or payment of a series of sums periodically over a stated number of time periods. Examples are rent and the flow of funds attached to a tax shield arising from depreciation.

There is much similarity between the mathematics already used and that which is necessary for *annuities,* as this type of periodic payment is termed by mathematicians. The focal date, however, takes on a new meaning, which the conventions of financial mathematics make even more complex. If one is looking into periods following the focal date, that date is the beginning of the first period of the annuity. In this case the applicable value at the focal date is zero, for the first payment of the annuity will take place only at the end of the first time period. If one is looking at times which are earlier than the focal date, however, the focal date is defined as the end of the last period, just after the moment of the final payment of the annuity. Again, the value is zero.

We shall introduce the annuity tables in the same order as before; that is, we first look ahead in time to consider the *compound amount* of an annuity, and then back to consider the *present value* of an annuity.

Compounding · Any annuity can be separated into a series of single payments and evaluated by the table of compound interest already described.

Suppose $1.00 is to be received at the end of each period, and that each $1.00 is to be invested at compound interest. How much will be the amount of the annuity a specified number of periods after the focal date? Let us take 4 percent and five years. The answer can be built up from Table 1, of compound amount, as follows:

$1.00 received at time +1 at 4% for 4 years becomes $1.170
1.00 received at time +2 at 4% for 3 years becomes 1.125
1.00 received at time +3 at 4% for 2 years becomes 1.082
1.00 received at time +4 at 4% for 1 year becomes 1.040
1.00 received at time +5 at 4% for 0 year becomes 1.000

Total Value, Amount of Annuity $5.417

From this example, we can see that a table of the desired values for annuities can be obtained by accumulating values from compound interest tables. See Table 3 for a brief portion of such a table.

TABLE 3

Amount of Annuity of $1.00 per Period

Periods	Rate 4%	Rate 10%
0	0	0
+1	1.000	1.000
+2	2.040	2.100
+3	3.122	3.310
+4	4.246	4.641
+5	5.416°	6.105

° The difference between this figure and 5.417, the amount of annuity given above, is due to rounding.

The question answered by such a table is: How much will the periodic receipt of $1.00 grow if all payments are held at compound interest at a specified rate and for a specified number of periods? In business terms, we are dealing with an annuity that is to be received.

Discounting · We now look at an annuity that is being paid out by the business, asking the question: How much must be invested in period $-n$ at the specified rate to permit the payment of an annuity of $1.00 per period, leaving nothing at the focal date? As before, this can be broken down into separate payments, which can be evaluated from the table of the present value of single sums. Let us take 4 percent and five years once more. Table 2 can be used.

At the beginning of period -5:
    it takes 0.822 to produce $1.00 in 5 years,
    it takes 0.855 to produce $1.00 in 4 years,
    it takes 0.889 to produce $1.00 in 3 years,
    it takes 0.925 to produce $1.00 in 2 years,
    it takes 0.962 to produce $1.00 in 1 year.

    Total 4.453, Value of Annuity at Period -5

This example shows how the desired present values of annuities can be obtained by accumulating values from the table of the present values of a single sum. Such a table is included in most books on finance. For convenience, we reproduce a portion in Table 4.

TABLE 4

PRESENT VALUE OF $1.00 RECEIVED PERIODICALLY FOR n PERIODS

Periods	Rate 4%	Rate 10%
0	0	0
−1	0.962	0.909
−2	1.886	1.736
−3	2.775	2.487
−4	3.630	3.170
−5	4.452*	3.791

* The difference between this figure and 4.453, the value of the annuity given above, is due to rounding.

When we were dealing with the changing values of a single sum over time, we ended our explanation with a diagram. A similar one, Chart 2, can be presented for annuities, although the situation is more complex. The reader will note, in studying the charted annuities, that the values get larger as one proceeds in either direction from the focal date. This is because of the periodic payments of $1.00 that are involved. The reader will also note here, as in the more simple case, that changing the rate of return has considerable influence on the values, especially as time becomes more remote. In each instance the higher the rate, the greater the advantage to the user of the funds. That is, if 10 percent is applied, an annuity will cost less, or produce more, than if a lower rate were applied.

Before we leave the subject of the present values of annuities, we shall describe in another way the operation of the investment of $4.452 at 4 percent to permit paying $1.00 per year for five years. This will not add to the theoretical structure, but it will picture the process in a way that is more useful in financial thinking.

At the beginning of year −5, invest $4.452.
At the end of year −5, take interest of $0.178, and withdraw $0.822.
At the beginning of year −4, remainder invested becomes $3.630.

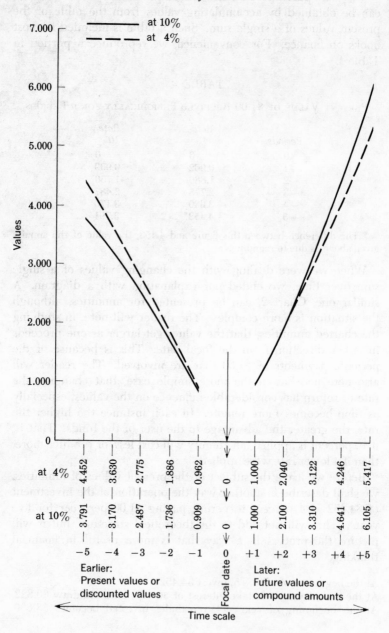

CHART 2

EFFECTS OF TIME ADJUSTMENT: ANNUITY

at 10%
at 4%

Values

7.000

6.000

5.000

4.000

3.000

2.000

1.000

0

| at 4% | 4.452 | 3.630 | 2.775 | 1.886 | 0.962 | 0 | 1.000 | 2.040 | 3.122 | 4.246 | 5.417 |

| at 10% | 3.791 | 3.170 | 2.487 | 1.736 | 0.909 | 0 | 1.000 | 2.100 | 3.310 | 4.641 | 6.105 |

| −5 | −4 | −3 | −2 | −1 | 0 | +1 | +2 | +3 | +4 | +5 |

Focal date

Earlier:
Present values or
discounted values

Later:
Future values or
compound amounts

Time scale

At the end of year −4, take interest of $0.145, and withdraw $0.855.
At the beginning of year −3, remainder invested becomes $2.775.
At the end of year −3, take interest of $0.111, and withdraw $0.889.
At the beginning of year −2, remainder invested becomes $1.886.
At the end of year −2, take interest of $0.075, and withdraw $0.925.
At the beginning of year −1, remainder invested becomes $0.961.
At the end of year −1, take interest of $0.038, and withdraw $0.962.
There is a difference between $0.962 and $0.961, because of the use of
abbreviated tables. Ignoring this, we can see that the annuity ends
with the final payment of $1.00.

From this table, it can be seen that a company can receive $1.00
a year for five years with an initial investment of $4.452, if the
interest rate is 4 percent. It can also be seen, however, that the
initial investment of capital is consumed in the process. It is of
great importance to recognize that the table does *not* say that if
the rate of return is 4 percent, the annuity will go on without
reducing principal. If the principal is to be preserved, its with-
drawals must not be consumed, but invested elsewhere. Also,
if 4 percent is to continue to be obtained from the use of funds,
the new investment opportunities must yield this rate.

Examples Using Annuities · As before, we conclude our explanation of the derivation of tables of compound amount and
present value for annuities with examples taken from business
situations.

Example 1. A firm which is considering setting up a pension
fund determines that it can afford to set aside for this purpose
$100,000 a year for ten years. It is advised that a trustee can
earn 4 percent (tax exempt) with such moneys. How much will
have been accumulated after ten years?

The problem is to evaluate an annuity of $100,000 whose focal
date is the present, whose period is ten years, and whose rate is
4 percent. Tables of compound amount (not available in this
book) give a factor of 12.006 under these conditions. Multiplying
by $100,000 gives the desired answer, which is $1,200,600.

Example 2. Analysis of a certain investment project indicates
that it will produce $50,000 a year, before taxes, for ten years.
How much could the company justify investing in this project if
other investments are available at 4 percent? At 10 percent?

The problem is the evaluation as of now of an annuity whose

focal date is ten years from the present. We find the present value factor for ten periods to be 8.111 for 4 percent, and 6.145 for 10 percent. Multiplying by $50,000, we find $405,550 for 4 percent and $307,250 for 10 percent. These are the sums that could be invested at the specified rates to produce $50,000 a year for ten years.

Example 3. Taking the figures as developed in Example 2, assume that the firm finds that $350,000 is required as an investment to establish the project. Since this number is more than the present value at 10 percent, the firm should not undertake the project if it has other opportunities on which 10 percent can be earned. The firm should, however, consider the project an excellent one if the alternative opportunities are offering 4 percent return.

Finding the Rate of Return · One last step in the use of present value tables will be illustrated here. Given the periodic amount of an annuity and the original investment, what is the rate of return? Using the figures from Example 3, above, what rate of return will produce a ten-year annuity of $50,000 from the investment of $350,000?

The focal date is the end of the ten-year period, when the last payment will be received. The present value table is based on annuities of $1.00 per period, so the figures in the actual case must be converted by dividing through by $50,000:

$$\frac{50,000}{50,000} = 1.000$$

and

$$\frac{350,000}{50,000} = 7.000.$$

Looking at the table of present values of an annuity for ten periods, we find:

Rate 6%. 7.360
Rate 8%. 6.710

By interpolation, the answer can be computed. It is 7.1 percent.

A Simple Example of Capital Budgeting

ALAN S. MANNE

Alan Manne is Professor of Economics at Stanford University. This article is from a chapter of his book, Economic Analysis for Business Decisions, *published in 1961.*

Perhaps the best way to understand what is involved in problems of economic choice is to start with a highly simplified model of what is ordinarily the most important of all corporate decisions—drawing up an investment budget. Typically, such a budget applies to a forthcoming calendar year, but it may refer to a two- or even a five-year period. Logically, the first step in this process consists of a forecast of the funds that will be available from internal sources of finance—primarily depreciation reserves and retained earnings. Suppose that this forecast works out as follows:

Retained earnings	$20 million
Depreciation reserves	10 million
Total funds available from internal sources	$30 million

The next step consists of a survey of investment opportunities among department heads and plant managers. For our purposes, we shall assume that there is only one criterion relevant to the problem of investment choice: expected dollar return on investment. In this crude model, we shall neglect the very real problem of evaluating riskiness and also of placing a dollar value upon investments in such intangibles as product development, employee morale, and community relations. The investment opportunities under survey will be presumed comparable in all respects, except the factor of percentage rate of return on investment. We can suppose that the results of our survey are as follows:

Per cent return on investment, per annum	Number of dollars' worth of projects, millions	Cumulative dollars' worth, millions
30	8	8
25	12	20
20	15	35
15	10	45

It is now an easy matter to see how the $30 million available from internal sources should be allocated among the different projects so as to maximize the total return. All those yielding 25 percent or more should be undertaken. Those yielding 15 percent or less should be eliminated. And of those yielding exactly 20 percent, just $10 million worth should be initiated. The "cutoff rate of return," or "implicit worth of capital," in this case is said to be 20 percent per annum. Another way to put this is to say that if just $30 million worth of funds were available, it would be possible to utilize as much as an additional $5 million before the incremental yield dropped below 20 percent.

Once this calculation has been performed, a number of interesting by-products emerge. For one thing, suppose that a new project, one not included in the original survey, is brought up for consideration, and suppose that the rate of return on this is only 13 percent. Clearly enough, since this return lies below the cutoff rate, the project can be dismissed from further consideration, assuming always that the rate of return is a suitable basis for ranking projects. Conversely, if a new 25 percent project arises, it will pay to undertake it, obtaining the funds by reducing the volume of investment planned at the 20 percent cutoff, or implicit, rate of return.

Possibly the most important use of the cutoff rate concept lies in raising questions about the adequacy of the internal financing that is available. As soon as it is apparent that the incremental, or "marginal," worth of capital is 20 percent, it is quite likely that the financial officers will be stimulated into thinking about ways of supplementing the existing sources of funds, e.g., to retain a larger share of earnings in the form of undistributed profits, or to draw down the investment in inventory, or to float new securities, or . . . . The implicit rate of return provides a means for comparing the efficacy of each of these alternatives.[1]

1. [For further discussions of capital budgeting, see "Measuring the Productivity of Capital" and E. Solomon, *The Management of Corporate Capital* (Chicago, 1959). *Editor*]

Measuring the Productivity of
Capital

JOEL DEAN

*Joel Dean is Professor of Business Economics
at Columbia University's Graduate School of
Business. This article comes from the* Harvard Business Review *of January 1954.*

The president of one of our largest oil companies, who was
pushing through a program of drastic decentralization of management, stated recently that the last thing he would delegate would
be decisions about capital expenditures. This is understandable
because capital-expenditure decisions form the framework for a
company's future development and are a major determinant of
efficiency and competitive power. The wisdom of these corporate
investment decisions, therefore, has a profound effect upon a
company's future earnings and growth.

From the standpoint of the stockholder and of the consumer,
capital expenditures are the principal bulwark against the seemingly endless progression of wage increases. From the standpoint
of labor, capital expenditures are the basic economic source of
future wage advances since they embody the creative forward
strides of advancing technology. Finally, capital expenditures,
both by their aggregate size and by their cyclical timing, have
a great deal to do with the character of the economy as a whole,
and thus with the government's role in maintaining stability.

MANAGEMENT PROGRAM

Farsighted judgment is an essential requisite for wise decisions about capital expenditures. But such judgment, to be sound, must be based on analysis of all the facts, many of them extremely technical and complex. In particular, top management needs an objective means of measuring the economic worth of individual investment proposals in order to have a realistic basis for choosing among them and selecting those which will mean the most to the company's long-run prosperity. The basic measure of economic worth is the productivity of capital, which means its power to produce profits. The purpose of this article is to suggest better ways of making that measurement.

Unfortunately, the problem of managing capital expenditure has not generally been attacked with the kind of thorough and objective analysis that has paid such big dividends in other management areas. I have made a study of the capital-expenditure methods of some fifty large companies. These are all well-managed companies so far as production, engineering, and marketing methods are concerned, and I have a great deal of admiration for their executives. But on capital expenditures they show widespread failure to measure the investment worth of individual proposals directly, lack of defensible objective standards of an acceptable investment, and distorted dedication to procedures and paper work, with inadequate understanding of the economic content of the concepts used. In other words, when it comes to capital expenditures, they are still forced to play by ear to a distressing extent.

The development of an effective system for managing capital expenditures requires a complex combination of disciplines: (*a*) application of economic theory at several vital points; (*b*) knowledge of financial mathematics, which most of us acquired in our apprenticeship days but have inevitably forgotten long since; (*c*) economic forecasting; (*d*) techniques for projecting the amount and timing of outlays and receipts; and (*e*) techniques of control through comparison of actualities with projections. Top management clearly needs technical help. No executive, even if he had the time to analyze each capital proposal personally, could be expected to have all the necessary disciplines at his command; they can only be gathered together in a team of specialists.

This article concentrates on the measurement of the economic worth of individual investment proposals. But we must remember that, though this is likely to be the critical element, it is only one of many components in a well-rounded program of capital management.

ARE PROFITS CONTROLLING?

As we turn, now, to the phase of capital-expenditure management that is our main concern here—measurement of capital productivity—we must face an underlying question: To what degree are investment decisions actually controlled by profit considerations?

Concern with capital productivity of course implies that the company's goal is profits. But actually in many cases money making is a secondary objective. Often the primary goal is strategic—to maintain or increase the company's share of the market, to achieve growth in sales volume or number of employees, or simply to build reputation and status. Often capital expenditures capture and embody this kind of motivation in the form of corporate monuments made "just to become the kind of company we want to be." I am thinking of welfare and prestige investments like gymnasiums, country clubs, and palatial offices.

A corporation is not single-minded. It is composed of groups and individuals whose interests conflict. The concept of management as arbiter among employees, customers, and stockholders can lead to capital-expenditure policies and commitments that stray from the directional beam of capital productivity. Not that this is necessarily wrong. But, at least, when a company does let such goals as welfare or prestige govern, it ought to know the cost of such a policy. The only way to find out this cost is to determine the profitability of capital projects and see how much profit is being passed up in order to build such corporate monuments. The cost of prestige, then, is the amount of earnings foregone by departing from a pattern of investment ruthlessly directed at profit maximization.

Even where money making does dominate, the theory that a company tries to maximize its profits needs some qualification. Much more prevalent is what can be described as the doctrine of *adequate profits.* Of course, when profits performance or outlook is inadequate, the stockholder's power does come into play and capital expenditures are likely to be oriented toward profit maximization. But so long as the company is making adequate profits, the drive to have all capital expenditures selected on the basis of profit maximization is blunted.

Thus, I am well aware that making maximum profits is often not the sole or even the dominant goal in managing capital expenditures. But that does not lessen the importance of being able to measure the productivity of capital (i.e., its power to produce profits). Moreover, my viewpoint here remains that of the missionary rather than the anthropologist. As in other applications of managerial economics, the objective is to help executives improve policies, not simply to report practice (or malpractice).

YARDSTICKS OF INVESTMENT WORTH

The heart of good capital-expenditure management, then, is the measurement of the investment worth of individual proposals. But in order to measure how good a project is, we must have the right kind of yardstick. Just what should a good yardstick do?

The productivity of capital can be indicated in several ways, but the central requirement of a good yardstick is that it should measure what the proposed outlay will do to earnings, and do this in a way that permits realistic comparison of one investment proposal with another. What we seek is a measuring rod which will help decide, for example, whether a $5,000 project that will earn $2,000 a year for three years is more attractive than a $60,000 project that will earn $10,000 a year for ten years.

A good yardstick of investment worth should summarize in a single figure all the information that is relevant to the decision whether or not to make the particular investment, and none that is irrelevant. It should be applicable to all types of proposals and should permit appraisal in terms of a single set of standards. Also, it should provide an index that is relatively simple to compute; once the basic data on the proposal have been assembled, the operating people should be able to measure the project's worth easily and without any need to explain how they do it.

Finally, the yardstick should permit simple adjustments to allow for ranges of uncertainty in the earnings estimates, since one of the facts to be taken into account is man's inability to see very far into the future with any great precision.

How do the three most commonly used yardsticks—(*a*) degree of necessity, (*b*) payback period, and (*c*) rate of return—stack up against those criteria?

Degree of Necessity · The degree of urgency of the proposed project—that is, the extent to which it cannot be postponed to later years—is one kind of yardstick for assigning priority to investment proposals. For example, a railroad might put a power crane replacement proposal ahead of a repair shop modernization request because the old crane had broken down and something had to be done about it immediately, whereas the repair shop project could wait.

Degree of necessity has a place in the capital budgeting scheme. Some investments must be made to meet requirements imposed by a government agency. Grade-crossing eliminations for railroads, sanitary facilities in food-processing plants, and mandatory smoke-control installations are examples. Other investments clearly must be made if the company is to remain in business, e.g., replacement of a washed-out section of a railroad's main line. In these cases the alternative is such that its adoption would have a catastrophic effect on the firm's profits. Projects of this nature seldom bulk large in a company's over-all capital-expenditure program.

A serious defect of degree of urgency is that it fails to measure the capital productivity of a proposal—that is, the effect it will have on the company's earnings. A plant-modernization project may be highly postponable; but if it can produce annual savings which will yield 30 percent on the added capital tied up, it is to be preferred to a less postponable but less profitable project. Or, replacement of a shop destroyed by fire may seem completely unpostponable, whereas actually the company might find its over-all profits enhanced by subcontracting the operations formerly performed in the destroyed facilities.

Moreover, the degree of urgency is not a measurable quantity. Proposed projects cannot be assembled and arranged in a single priority ladder; acceptance standards cannot be set up to choose wisely among projects submitted on a necessity basis.

The most serious result of accepting or rejecting proposals primarily on the basis of how urgent they seem to be is that the capital budgeting program is likely to degenerate into a contest of personalities. The biggest share of the capital-expenditure money will go to the division heads who are the most eloquent or most persistent in presenting their requests, rather than to those who have taken the time and effort necessary to make an objective appraisal of the project's economic worth. The result is that all projects come up for review in an atmosphere of haste and emergency, with full scope allowed for the arts of persuasion and exhortation. Not only will projects whose economic desirability is dubious be pushed through to acceptance, but also a large proportion of investments that would yield big savings and high profits may be put off almost indefinitely.

Payback Period · The yardstick of payback period—that is, the number of years required for the earnings on the project to pay back the original outlay with no allowance for capital wastage— is unquestionably the most widely used measure of investment worth. Payback is superior to postponability since it takes into consideration the projected gross earnings, and it does have certain uses in capital-expenditure management:

Payback can serve as a coarse screen to pick out high-profit projects that are so clearly desirable as to require no refined rate-of-return estimates and to reject quickly those projects which show such poor promise that they do not merit thorough economic analysis. In addition, it may be adequate as a measure of investment worth for companies with a high outside cost of capital and severely limited internal cash-generating ability in comparison with the volume of highly profitable internal investment opportunities. If a shortage of funds forces the company to accept only proposals which promise a payback period after taxes of two years or less, the use of a more refined measure might not affect the list of accepted projects.

It also can be useful for appraising risky investments where the rate of capital wastage is particularly hard to predict. Since payback weights near-year earnings heavily and distant earnings not at all, it contains a sort of built-in hedge against the possibility of a short economic life.

For most corporations, however, payback is an inadequate measure of investment worth. It is a cash concept, designed to answer the single question of how soon the cash outlay can be returned to the company's treasury. As such it fails in three important respects to provide a satisfactory yardstick for appraising all the profit-producing investments of a firm:

1. Payback tends to overweight the importance of liquidity as a goal of the capital-expenditure program. No firm can ignore needed liquidity. But most can achieve it by means that are more direct and less costly than sacrificing profits by allowing payback to govern the selection of capital projects.

2. It ignores capital wastage. By confining analysis to the project's gross earnings (before depreciation) it takes no cognizance of its probable economic life.

3. It fails to consider the earnings of a project after the initial outlay has been paid back. By concentrating on liquidity, it ignores the vital matter of what the life pattern of the earnings will be. Up to the end of the payback period the company has just got its bait back. How much longer the earnings will last is what determines the profitability of the investment. A three-year payback project may yield a 30 percent return on average investment if it has a long life, but only 12 percent if its life is four years, and no return at all if just three years.

In short, because payback does not measure or reflect all the dimensions of profitability which are relevant to capital expenditure decisions, it is neither inclusive enough nor sensitive enough to be used as the company's over-all measure of investment worth.

Rate of Return · Measurement of the economic worth of an investment proposal by means of rate of return relates the project's anticipated earnings to the amount of funds which will be tied up during the investment life of the facility. Rate of return embodies the concept of *net* earnings after allowing for capital wastage. Neither degree of necessity nor payback period uses this concept, since payback is measured in terms of gross earnings, and urgency does not consider earnings at all.

Rate of return has its shortcomings. A sound rate-of-return

system is more complex than most of the methods of rationing a corporation's capital that are in current use. It costs more to install and put into operation. Also it may run into obstacles because it is unfamiliar and possibly because it will block privileged channels from access to capital funds.

But such limitations should not be decisive. Good management of capital expenditures is too vital to be blocked by ignorance, caution, or smugness. Overcoming the old organization's natural resistance to learning new tricks and training it in a new pattern of thought about capital expenditures is a one-shot affair. Once the system is installed, very little effort and cost are needed to keep it going.

The positive superiorities of a rate-of-return measure of investment worth are imposing. It takes account of the full lifetime of a capital-expenditure proposal. Two projects, each of which shows a three-year payback, may differ greatly in the length of time for which they will produce earnings for the company. Take this experience which one company had:

Certain refinery equipment that showed a three-year payback actually became obsolete and was replaced in less than three years. This project's rate of return, therefore, was less than zero, despite what appeared to be a very satisfactory payback. In contrast, a pipeline that had the same three-year payback kept on earning (and promises to continue for twenty years more). Clearly its rate of return was much higher.

Capital wastage—that is, the gradual loss of the economic value of the facility over a period of time—is of vital importance in the appraisal of an investment proposal. Capital productivity should be measured by earnings over the whole life of the investment, even though estimates of the distant future may be subject to wide margins of error.

Because rate of return considers the full life of an investment proposal, correct comparisons of the degree of value of projects can be made. Proposals can therefore be arranged in a ladder of priority even where they seem to be of the same degree of urgency or to have the same payback period. Moreover, the fact that the projects themselves may differ widely in their characteristics does not impede the comparison. New-product investments can thus be compared with cost-reducing projects; or a proposal this year can be compared with one which will not be ready until next year.

Better standards of rejection are made possible by rate of return. A company's combined cost of capital—say, 15 percent—can be used to determine the proper rate of cutoff on the capital-demand ladder just discussed; i.e., the minimum acceptable profitability of a proposal. This not only provides an objective, defensible basis for acceptance or rejection; it also aids top management in delegating authority by providing sound bench marks for personnel down the line to use in killing off the worst propositions before they have gone far up the chain of command.

Finally, rate-of-return rationing is likely to produce more earnings for stockholders, since it directs the flow of funds to their most profitable use by measuring the productivity of capital correctly and comparing it with a relevant standard of acceptable profitability.

MAKING THE ESTIMATES

We have seen that for most companies rate of return is the best yardstick of economic worth. Two problems arise in the practical application of this yardstick. The first concerns the concept for making the empirical projections that are needed to get the three basic determinants of project worth: (a) earnings, (b) economic life, and (c) amount of capital tied up. The second problem (discussed later) is how to combine these determinants in an index of profitability.

Ten Fallacies · The part of this measurement problem which is most often muffed is the job of getting a clear idea of just what needs to be estimated. Why should there be any problem in clarifying the concepts for rate-of-return measurement? The nature of the difficulties and their importance for good measurement can be seen by looking at ten common fallacies.

1. *"No Alternatives."* Perhaps the most common mistake in analyzing a capital proposal is the failure to consider any alternatives. There are always alternatives to an investment proposal, and a systematic analysis of the alternatives is the bench mark for estimating both the investment and the earnings of a capital

project. What will happen if the requested investment is not made measures what the company will get out of it if the investment is made. If, as usual, there are several alternatives differing in the amount of investment required, earnings estimates should logically be built upon the smallest investment alternative which is acceptably profitable. Alternatives which require greater investment are preferable to this one only if the *added* investment over this amount produces enough *added* earnings to yield a satisfactory rate of return.

2. "*'Must' Investment.*" Closely related is the "must" investment fallacy. The common conviction that certain equipment replacements are indispensable for continuing operations implies that top management has no alternatives. True, the alternative is sometimes so catastrophic that it is academic. But even in such a case the reason for making the investment should not be that it is urgent or indispensable, but that its profitability is terrific measured against the catastrophic alternative. Thus the rate of return from replacing a burnt-out pump in an oil pipeline may be astronomical; the investment is small and its earnings are the profits from the whole line, since the only alternative is a complete shutdown.

High-profit investments of this special nature are rarer than realized. Skeptical study of supposed "must" investments will reveal alternatives to many of them and will show that some of them are neither necessary nor even acceptably profitable.

3. "*High Strategy.*" Another fallacy is the notion that some projects are so pivotal for the long-run welfare of the enterprise that they possess high strategic value which overrides mere economic considerations and lifts their evaluation into a mystic realm beyond the ken of economic and financial analysis. For example, the dogma that an integrated oil company should own 75 percent of its crude oil sometimes precludes economic analysis of integration investments.

It is true that some capital expenditures do have benefits which are hard to measure because they are diffused over a wide area of company activity or because they stretch over a protracted time period. And there are some investments which must be made on almost pure faith (e.g., a new research center). Nevertheless, the idea that there is such a thing as strategic value not ultimately rooted in economic worth is demonstrably wrong. If a contemplated investment produces results that do not have any economic value, then directors and stockholders should question its wisdom.

4. *"Routine Replacement."* This fallacy maintains that scheduled periodic replacement of capital facilities is a practical and inexpensive substitute for an investment analysis of the economic desirability of individual replacements. For example, many fleet owners replace motor trucks on a routine basis (i.e., after a certain number of years or a certain number of miles), without determining whether the added net earnings from replacing this or that old truck with a new one will produce an adequate return on the specific added investment. Routine replacement has the virtues of simplicity, orderliness, and predictability. But vintage retirement will not produce as profitable a pattern of investment as will a capital-earnings plan.

5. *"Prediction is Impossible."* Scoffers maintain that since the future cannot be predicted with accuracy, it is futile to try to guess the useful life of a proposed facility or to project its earnings beyond the first year. The consequence of this fallacy is an unwillingness to define concepts in a way that will force explicit projection. People try to duck out by proclaiming that "with a four-year payback, it doesn't matter" or by embracing "unfair" Bureau of Internal Revenue depreciation rates.

The basic mistake is refusing to recognize that forecasting, though difficult and subject to error, is nevertheless necessary in appraising the worth of capital projects. Prediction, whether or not it is done consciously, lies at the heart of any executive judgment about a proposed investment. Usually it is better to *know* what is being done.

6. *"Fair Share of Overhead."* A common error in project analysis is to use allocations of current overhead instead of estimating the added costs that will be caused by the project. This cost-proration fallacy confuses problems of equity with problems of economic consequences. This is illustrated by a question frequently raised: Should a new product line, acquisition of which is being contemplated, carry its full share of the overhead now borne by mature products, or should it get a free ride? Neither of these suggested solutions is correct, at least for estimating project earnings. Old

overheads do not matter—only new overheads. What is needed is not a reallocation of past overheads but a forecast of how future overheads will increase by acceptance as opposed to rejection of the project. This cost increment is wholly unaffected by the conventions of apportionment of common costs.

7. *"Free Ride."* A related fallacy that frequently misguides analysis of capital proposals errs in the opposite direction. It holds that new products or added volume are "plus business" in the sense of incurring negligible additional costs. This "free ride" fallacy leads to the conclusion that earnings from expansion investments are almost equivalent to their revenue. There is something to this notion; long-run incremental costs are often smaller than fully allocated average costs. But they are larger than short-run marginal costs and never negligible.

While short-run marginal costs are relevant for operating decisions, long-run added costs must be used for investment decisions. Herein lies the peril of the "free ride" fallacy. What, for instance, are the earnings from an added gasoline service station when pipeline and bulk plant capacities will just take that added volume? If only the marginal cost of using this bulk-movement capacity is included, rate of return is high. But continued normal growth will soon force expansion of the bulk-movement capacity; the new service station brings this time that much closer. If the full cost of this expansion is included in estimating lifetime earnings, the return of course shows up as much lower.

8. *"Carrying Charge."* The practice of charging the earnings of all projects with an interest cost might be called the "carrying charge" fallacy. Usually this charge is computed by applying the company's short-term borrowing rate to the capitalized portion of the original investment. This approach has the virtue of recognizing that money is not costless, even though no entry is made in the accounts. It has, however, two defects: (*a*) it uses the wrong cost of money, since high-cost equity capital is left out, and (*b*) it introduces cost of money into the capital-management program in the wrong way. Instead of subtracting carrying costs from individual projects, it is better to use cost of capital as a cutoff rate to select acceptably profitable projects.

9. *"Book Value."* Determination of the investment amount looks so easy that it is often done wrong. Bookkeeping is the root

of error here. Accounting conventions that are indispensable for financial reporting give the wrong steer for estimating a project's investment base. The test of what should be included in the investment amount is not how it is handled on the books, which bears only on the tax effects of the proposal, an important but quite separate issue. The test is whether or not the outlay is necessary to produce the stream of earnings contemplated in the proposal.

The "book value" concept would exclude outlays that are expensed (rather than capitalized) from the amount of investment serving as the base for the rate-of-return estimate. Take a proposal to convert an unused portion of a building into a sausage factory requiring $100,000 of capitalizable machinery plus $150,-000 of expensed repairs. The pretax investment amount is the whole $250,000; after deflating the expensed portion for 50 percent income tax rates ($150,000 minus $75,000), the after-tax investment amount is seen to be $175,000. But the book value is only $100,000.

Book value also gives bad investment guidance in propping up, transferring, or abandoning existing assets. The book value of an existing asset is based on recorded historical cost less accumulated depreciation. For investment decisions, its value should be determined by what the company can get for the asset or what the company can do with it in its next best internal use, rather than by the figures that happen to be on the books.

10. *"Taxes Don't Matter."* There is a surprisingly widespread conviction that adjustment for corporate income taxes is academic. This "taxes don't matter" fallacy assumes that the underlying worth of a project is obscured (rather than revealed) by allowing for tax effects, and that the ranking of capital products will be the same whether or not they are deflated for taxes. This beguiling notion is wrong in two respects: (*a*) In order to apply tenable acceptance standards such as the company's outside cost of capital, it is necessary to measure rate of return after taxes, rather than before taxes. (*b*) The impact of taxes differs depending on the time shape of the project; and the after-tax ranking of proposals will differ significantly from their before-tax ranking if taxes are correctly taken into account in computing rate of return. For example, the tax effects of accelerated amortization can con-

vert a border-line project into a highly profitable investment opportunity.

Positive Concepts · Having looked at these ten fallacies, we are in a better position to formulate positive concepts of what needs to be estimated in measuring project earnings and project investment.

A correct estimate of earnings must be based on the simple principle that the earnings from a proposal are measured by the total *added* earnings or savings from making the investment as opposed to not making it. The proper bench mark for computing earnings on a project is the *best alternative* way of doing the job; comparison therewith will indicate the source and amount of the added earnings. Project costs should be unaffected by allocations of existing overheads but should cover all the changes in total overhead (and other) costs that are forecasted to result from the investment, but nothing else—nothing that will be the same regardless of whether the proposal is accepted or rejected.

The value of a proposed investment depends on its future earnings. Hence, the earnings estimate should be based on the best available projections of future volume, wage rates, and price levels. Earnings should be estimated over the economic life of the proposed facilities. Because project earnings vary in time shape, and because this will affect the rate of return, the earnings estimates should reflect the variations in the time trend of earnings.

In estimating economic life of an investment, consideration must be given to (*a*) physical deterioration, (*b*) obsolescence, and (*c*) the possibility that the source of earnings will dry up before either of the first two factors becomes operative.

Interest on investment should not be deducted from project earnings. Charging interest increases the complexity of the rate-of-return computation without adding to the information it provides. Earnings should be stated after corporate income taxes, for only in such form are they relevant for capital attraction and for dividend payment.

The appropriate investment base for calculating rate of return is the added outlay which is occasioned by the adoption of the project as opposed to rejecting it and adopting an alternative which requires less investment. The entire amount of the original added outlay should be included in the investment amount, regardless of how it is treated in the books. Any tax benefit which results from expensing certain items rather than capitalizing them should be reflected. Those repairs which would be made whether or not the proposal is adopted should be excluded from the investment amount, because they are not caused by it.

If the proposal involves a transfer of facilities from another part of the company, the opportunity cost of these facilities (the amount foregone by using them this way rather than another) should be added to the amount of investment. If the opportunity foregone is merely to sell the facilities for scrap, then this will indicate the value to set on the transferred assets.

The amount of the investment should also include the amount of any additional necessary investment in working capital or other auxiliary facilities. Research and promotional expenses to get new products rolling or to develop new methods or to expand business are no less investments than plant and equipment.

CALCULATING RATE OF RETURN

Once the basic estimates of project earnings and investment have been made, there are two major ways of combining them into a rate-of-return measurement. One way—which can be called the "accounting method" because it is closely related to many of the concepts used in conventional accounting procedure—computes rate of return as the ratio of (a) the project's earnings averaged over the life of the proposition to (b) the average lifetime investment. The other—which can be called "discounted cash flow"—computes rate of return as the maximum interest rate which could be paid on the capital tied up over the life of the investment without dipping into earnings produced elsewhere in the company.

Accounting Method · A characteristic of the accounting method is that it has many variants, each of which produces a different rate-of-return figure for any one investment proposal. One set of variants comes from diverse concepts of the investment amount (e.g., the original outlay, $100,000, versus the average amount tied up in the facility over its life, $50,000). Another source of variants is the diverse concepts of the project earnings. Earnings can be either gross or net of depreciation, either before or after taxes. They can be the average for several years or for the first year only. This variety of alternatives produces a tremendous range of rate-of-return results. But they all fall into the category of accounting method, provided the final result is a ratio of earnings to investment.

This shortcoming can be minimized only by arbitrarily standardizing on one variant of the method and making all computations according to this standard.

A more serious drawback to the use of the accounting method is that it is insensitive to variations in the time pattern of investment outlays and earnings. By taking an annual average of earnings over the life of a project this method ignores the earning trends, which may be quite important.

The economic worth of an investment will be affected by the time shape of its lifetime earnings, because near money has greater economic value than distant money. For example, an oil well has a strikingly different time shape than a service station. A well which comes in as a gusher trails off to a pumper. In contrast, a service station in a new area has a rising curve of earnings and is likely to show post-operative losses in the first year or so. Failure to reflect these time-shape disparities in the index of investment worth leads to unprofitable capital-expenditure decisions.

The effect of time shape on economic worth is especially great when the company's cost of capital is high or when the foregone earnings on projects that are passed up are high. Only a company whose investment projects are roughly similar in time shape and in economic life can ignore this feature. For such a firm the added accuracy of the discounted-cash-flow method probably does not justify the transitional pain and effort required to install the system. But any company which has projects that vary significantly in either time shape or longevity has an important stake in using the most sensitive rate-of-return method available.

Discounted Cash Flow · The mechanics of the cash-flow method consist essentially of finding the interest rate that discounts future earnings of a project down to a present value equal to the project cost. This interest rate is the rate of return on that investment. Exhibit 1 illustrates the way in which rate of return can be determined under the cash-flow method for a cost-reducing machine which costs $2,200 and has an anticipated life of five years with no salvage value at the end of that time. In this case, an interest rate of 20 percent is found to make the present value of the future earnings stream equal to the present cost of the machine, so this is the rate of return.

EXHIBIT 1

CASH-FLOW METHOD OF COMPUTING RATE OF RETURN ILLUSTRATED
*(Machine costing $2,200 with anticipated life of five years
and no salvage value at the end of that time)*

| Year | Gross earnings before depreciation | Present value of earnings discounted at | | |
		18%	20%	22%
1	$ 200	$ 184	$ 182	$ 180
2	600	458	446	432
3	800	510	486	462
4	1,200	640	596	556
5	1,200	534	488	448
Total	$4,000	$2,326	$2,198	$2,078

Conceptually, this method is based on the principle that in making an investment outlay we are actually buying a series of future annual incomes—ranging in the example in the exhibit from $200 the first year to $1,200 by the fourth and fifth years. We have an investment in each of those incomes, an investment which compounds in value through time until its own year arrives and it materializes in cash earnings. Thus, for example, the $596 present value of the fourth year's earnings at 20 percent is the amount that would have to be invested at 20 percent now to yield $1,200 gross earnings during the fourth year ($596 compounded at 20 percent for three and one-half years—since the $1,200 would begin to come in at the beginning of the fourth year).

The basic simplicity of this method is brought out by this illustration. Earnings are stated as gross cash receipts (not figuring depreciation). Therefore, it is not necessary to allocate the cost of the machine over its life before computing return. Depreciation is allowed for automatically because the interest rate that discounts the sum of present values to zero is the rate of return on the investment after annual provisions for repaying the principal amount. We are not, as in the accounting method, watching the write-off of original cost; we are watching instead the growth of our investment outlay as we compound it through time.

The method is *simplified* by the fact that there is no need to make a decision as to which earnings base to use (e.g., original outlay, average investment, and so on), nor is there any need to enter interest as a direct cost of the project. Once the data are gathered and set up, there is only one rate-of-return answer possible, and it can be arrived at by straightforward working of charts and interest tables.[1]

Net Superiority of Discounted Cash Flow · The accounting method does have the advantage of familiarity and transparency. Although education would be necessary to get everyone to standardize on one method of averaging earnings and investment, the idea of computing a simple ratio by dividing one number by another is familiar to anyone who went beyond the second grade.

The discounted-cash-flow method admittedly is less familiar. While a method essentially similar to this has been widely used throughout the financial community for computing bond yields, insurance premiums, and rates on leased facilities where accuracy is important and even small errors may cause serious loss, it is new in its application to the measurement of productivity of individual capital-expenditure projects in industry. Hence the job of explaining it to the bookkeeper and the clerk will require time and effort. But its appearance of complexity is deceptive. Once the basic method is understood, it is actually simpler and quicker to use than the accounting method.

Another deterrent to its use is the fact that it does not correspond to accounting concepts about the recording of costs and revenues, so that special analysis is necessary to compute a postmortem on an investment made in the past. But this seems minor in comparison with its imposing superiorities:

1. The discounted-cash-flow method is economically realistic in confining the analysis to cash flows and forgetting about cus-

1. [Cases do arise where the rate of return is not unique. See the references in fn. 2 below. *Editor*]

tomary book allocations. The books, although very valuable for other purposes, are irrelevant for the task of measuring investment worth.

2. The use of this method forces guided thinking about the whole life of the project and concentration on the lifetime earnings.

3. It weights the time pattern of the investment outlay and the cash earnings from that outlay in such a way as to reflect real and important differences in the value of near and distant cash flows.

4. It reflects accurately and without ambiguity the timing of tax savings, either from expensing part of the investment outlay or from writing off capitalized costs over the life of the invest-ment—something quite difficult to do by the accounting method.

5. It permits simple allowances for risks and uncertainties and can be adapted readily to increasing the risk allowance over time.

6. It is strictly comparable to cost-of-capital ratios so that deci-sions can be made quickly and safely on the basis of the rela-tionship between indicated rate of return and the value of money to the company.

CONCLUSION

Examination of the capital-expenditure policies and procedures of some fifty well-managed companies shows that top manage-ment is forced to a distressing degree to rely on intuition and authority. Management lacks the skilled analysis and the scien-tific control needed for sound judgment on these intricate, vital capital decisions. The pivotal problem of capital-expenditure management is the measurement of the investment worth of individual proposals.

Systematic exploration to assure that investment opportunities are ferreted out and objectively analyzed is a prerequisite for the measurement of investment worth. Long-range capital plans and projections enable management to appraise projects in better perspective and to fit them into broader patterns. The comprehen-sive short-range capital budget which forecasts the timing of prob-able cash outlays for investment and the timing of cash inflows is essential for determining cut-off points by cash-generation criteria.

For orderly operation of rate-of-return rationing, management needs not only good management of capital productivity but also objective and defensible standards of minimum acceptability. These should generally be based on the company's cost of capital. Candid and economically realistic post-completion audits are indispensable incentives for measuring project profitability accurately; they also provide the systematized experience for improving project measurement in the future.

Special forms and procedures to implement these capital-expenditure management principles also need to be tailored to the particular conditions of the individual company. Above all, good capital-expenditure management must operate in an enlightened intellectual environment throughout the company; all the personnel concerned should understand the economics of capital expenditures and of the measurements and controls which a sound program entails.

For most companies, productivity of capital should be measured by rate of return, rather than by payback or degree of necessity. Estimates of a project's rate of return should be based on concepts of capital investment and projects earnings, which are indicated by what would happen if the company were to go ahead on the project instead of selecting some alternative which requires a smaller investment.

Prediction is essential; project worth depends solely on future earnings—the added earnings that will result from the added investment. These future earnings need to be forecasted over the whole economic life of the facility. Project costs should be unaffected by allocations of existing overhead, but should include all increases in overhead (and in other costs) that will be caused by the project. Earnings should be deflated for taxes. The investment base should be the entire added outlay regardless of bookkeeping —adjusted for corporate income taxes.

The discounted-cash-flow method of computing rate of return is demonstrably superior to existing alternatives in accuracy, realism, relevance, and sensitivity. Acceptance of rate-of-return capital budgeting should not hinge on willingness or reluctance to go this far in breaking with traditional methods.[2]

2. [For further discussion of criteria for choosing investments, see J. Lorie and L. Savage, "Three Problems in Rationing Capital" (1955), E. Solomon, "The Arithmetic of Capital Budgeting Decisions" (1956), and E. Renshaw, "A Note on the Arithmetic of Capital Budgeting Decisions" (1957), all in the *Journal of Business. Editor*]

Business and Economic Forecasting

Business Week

The following selection is an abridgement of an article which appeared in the September 24, 1955 issue of Business Week.

Many economists—among them some who have physically left the academic cloisters—still regard economic forecasting as a low and disreputable pursuit for learned men. "We don't know enough about the past to know anything much about the future," they say. So, they suggest, business must wait another hundred years or so before it can expect the savants to say anything meaningful about the future. Meanwhile, they maintain, it is proper that they should qualify all statements about the future to the point of meaninglessness.

But the number of economists who hold to this pure patient view of their calling is shrinking. More and more of them feel that if economics is to have any pretense of being a useful study its claim must rest on its ability to predict developments, and to provide solid foundations for policymakers to build on.

One of the chief reasons for the fact that more of them are overcoming their inhibitions about forecasting, and are concentrating on improving its techniques, is that they are being immersed deeper and deeper in government and business, where eyes are always on the future.

It would take volumes to explain all the forecasting techniques used these days. It is possible, though, to take up the chief techniques that economists use when they are working with any of the three basic strategies of forecasting.

TREND EXTRAPOLATION

Extrapolation is a six-bit word borrowed from the mathematicians. In this case it means predicting the future movements of an economic factor by projecting into the future the trends you know it has taken in the past. On a chart, an extrapolation looks like this:

CHART A

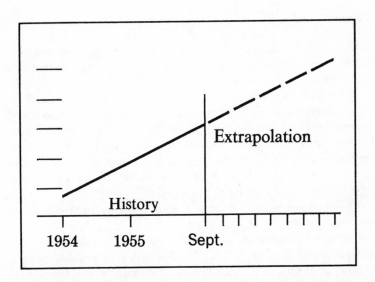

What makes an extrapolation useful to a forecaster is the statistical fact that a trend that is advancing will keep advancing—at least until something else happens. Unfortunately, the technique won't tell you when the "something else" will come. For instance, a wage series that is pushing upward will tend to push prices upward, and that will tend to push wages up again—only not ad infinitum. Eventually, some other series, like a falling sales volume, may halt or reverse the upward wage-price spiral.

But if, in your business, you don't need to care much about cyclical swings around a trend—if, for instance, you are figuring out the number of telephones or kilowatt hours the American people will want to use in the next ten years—trend extrapolation is a useful technique.

Of course, you can put trend extrapolation to work in a more sophisticated way than simply by laying a ruler over the past direction of a business indicator and projecting it on into the future. If you sell books or whiskey you may find your sales correlate nicely with the trend of disposable personal income, or if you sell oil or copper your sales may link up well with the Federal Reserve Index of Production.

"LEADING" SERIES

Andrew Carnegie constructed his own leading series for economic forecasting—by counting the smoking factory chimneys he saw. His was the archetype of the technique.

In the 1920s a hot search was on for a sort of economic philosopher's stone—a single business indicator that would always lead general business development. Some thought it lay in stock market activity; others saw it in interest rates, pig iron production, carloadings, or Dun & Bradstreet's index of business failures. Debate still rages over which of these are "old wives' indicators" and which possess real leading characteristics.

The outstanding hunter for indicators with forecasting value is the National Bureau of Economic Research. It has been scrutinizing masses of business-cycle data for more than three decades. Before World War II, Wesley C. Mitchell, the bureau's guiding genius, and Arthur F. Burns, later chairman of the Council of Economic Advisers under President Eisenhower, examined hundreds of series and picked a set of twenty-one leading, coincident, and lagging indicators, whose movements had regularly traced the course of the business cycle.

After the war, the bureau's Geoffrey H. Moore set to work updating Mitchell's and Burns's work. Moore examined 801 monthly and quarterly indicators and selected twenty-one, some of which were the same as those chosen by Mitchell and Burns. Of the twenty-one, Moore's eight leading series are: residential building contracts, commercial and industrial building contracts, new orders for durable goods, prices of industrial common stocks, wholesale prices of basic commodities, average work week in manufacturing, new incorporations, and business failures.

These indicators do regularly lead the business cycle's turns—though there is argument over just why this happens. But the chief trouble with them is that they are all extremely sensitive. They oscillate a great deal from month to month. So it is hard to know, when making a forecast, whether an up or downturn in one or another of the leading series means the real McCoy, or whether it is only a temporary wiggle.

DIFFUSION INDEXES

To find the meaning of those upturns and downturns, the bureau has invented the diffusion index. The bureau developed the index after it discovered that business cycle movements "have invariably been preceded by a remarkably regular cycle in the proportion of industrial activities undergoing expansion or contraction."

Forecasters make the index by counting the number of indicators in a given group that are rising at a given time. They convert this into a percentage of the number of indicators in the group. The bureau labels this percentage as a diffusion index because it believes it shows how widely diffused economic movements are. The bureau's diffusion indexes generally reach their peaks and troughs six months to twelve months ahead of the peaks and troughs of general business activity.

Not all economists think the diffusion index is much of a step forward. Arthur L. Broida, a Federal Reserve Board economist, maintains that it isolates cyclical turning points from all other changes in the economy's direction some time after the event. He holds that the index shows nothing different from what statisticians have long achieved by noting rates of growth and decline of a series of indicators. Their notes have already shown that a slower rate of increase in an index generally precedes its downturn.

SYSTEMATIC FORECASTING

Test-tube or systematic forecasting is the classic strategy of economic analysis. The technique here is to discover enduring relationships among economic factors and apply them to situations in the past, present, or future.

Analyzing the general business picture and making quantitative estimates of what conditions may be like a year or more ahead requires all the theoretical training, knowledge of institutional and statistical facts, technical skill, and political insight that an economist can command.

In dealing with comprehensive forecasting problems, economists today have two tremendous advantages over those who worked twenty years ago.

The first is economics' own "unified field theory." It is the product of the Keynesian revolution. Before John M. Keynes wrote his *General Theory of Employment, Interest, and Money,* economic theory tended to be fragmented into separate theories of wages, money, foreign trade, and so on. None of these separate principles had much relationship to each other. Economists may argue how much of the Keynesian revolution is attributable to Keynes himself. But there can be little doubt that general comprehension of how all the parts of an economy mesh together has advanced greatly since the mid–1930s.

The second advantage is the system of national income accounts developed since the early 1930s by the Commerce Department and the National Bureau of Economic Research. These give the economist a detailed and comprehensive picture of the national economy.

From unified economic theory and national income accounting stem the two most important techniques for systematic economic forecasting.

The "lost horse" technique is the first. That, anyway, is how it was christened by Sidney Alexander. He took the name from the old gag about how to find a lost horse. You do it by going to where the horse was last seen and asking yourself where you would go from there if you were a horse.

When you take that theory off the farm and put it to work in general business forecasting, each component of the gross national product (consumption, expenditures, gross private domestic investment, net foreign investment, government purchases of goods and services) plays the part of the lost horse. The analyst first finds out where each of these was when last reported by the Commerce Department's National Income Division.

But how he answers the question of where each section of GNP is going depends on his skill, patience, insight, and information

An economist who wants to fake impressively can simply guess figures for each part of the coming year's GNP. (Projecting gross private domestic investment at $49.6 billion is obviously more impressive than projecting it at $50 billion.) If there were state licensing boards for economists, a forecaster caught doing this would be convicted of malpractice and sentenced to run a checkout register in a supermarket for the rest of his days.

But the honest economist will go deeply behind each component of GNP when he prepares his forecast. He will study government plans and policies, analyze budget estimates, weigh the likelihood of the passage of important legislation and attempt to estimate the price tags the various bills will bear.

He will look behind private investment at the factors affecting the capital goods industries, study ratios of inventories to sales and of production to capacity. He will look at the factors that affect building construction, such as credit terms, availability of mortgage money, vacancy rates, rents, and price movements. He will measure his analysis against the findings of capital spending surveys.

He will try to gauge the effect of government fiscal policies on private investment and consumption, estimate the relationship between the growth of investment and consumption. Then he will see how money credit conditions may affect people's spending or saving, their liquid assets, their supplies of durable goods. And he will measure this against the finding of consumer intention surveys.

He must put all these parts together to make a whole—but he must also carry in his mind an image of how the whole will affect the parts. He will also have to sense how non-economic factors— like international relations and national elections—will affect the picture.

Since the task of preparing a forecast of the national economy can be almost endless, the economist must figure out the point at which he has all the information he can handle. But, at best, the time he has for these analyses is always pretty short, since he must base his forecasts on the most current information. If he takes too long, his facts grow cold. The best course for the forecaster is to stay at his task continuously, constantly modifying his forecast on the basis of new information.

The only way to judge whether an economist has done a thoroughly sensitive forecast—or blooped his way through one—is to examine carefully the details of his analysis. Of course, a lost horse analysis depends a lot on the economist's subjective judgments about the data he receives and on his somewhat "artistic" perception of relations. So all of his analysis may not show on paper.

A more rigorous way of tackling the problem of what will happen to the millions of factors and relations that make up the national economy is to build an econometric model of the economy. The method here is related to the lost-horse technique, but it is a lot more elegant, for the practice of econometrics is one of blending economics, mathematics, and statistics.

An economist starts to build a model by first selecting an economic theory, or set of theories, that he believes will take into account all the significant factors likely to affect the general business or particular industry situation that he is forecasting.

He translates the theory into a set of mathematical equations that make up his econometric model. The equations relate the factors he wants to discover (the dependent variables) to the factors he already knows, or can estimate easily (the independent variables). These independent variables can be of two types: first, those that are historic facts, such as last year's profits or inventory spending; and second, future elements, such as government spending, that can be estimated from advance information.

The econometrician bases his forecast on the past relations between the dependent and independent variables. He assumes that relations that were stable in the past will remain stable in the future. Of course, the relation between large economic aggregates, like consumption and income, won't be perfectly stable. So the question the forecaster must first answer is: "Will they be stable enough, within some estimated range of probability, to be used for forecasting?" If it turns out that they aren't stable enough for the job they are supposed to perform, the forecaster can assume that the theory behind his equations is not valid. Even then he has achieved something—and, in this way, econometrics can be a useful technique for junking false economic theories.

Econometric models come in for plenty of criticism from forecasters who stick to other techniques.

One of the chief complaints against them is that they make complex mathematical operations on data that is too rough to permit such manipulation. Stephen M. DuBrul, a General Motors economist, says that to apply intricate econometric techniques to the rough data that is available is "gold-plating crowbars."

But econometricians keep building their models and trying to improve them. They try to fit more factors into their figuring to overcome the complaints that their models are mechanically unsound and insensitive to social movements.

There are plenty of econometric model-builders at work to handle this task of improvement.

At Michigan University's Research Seminar in Quantitative Economics, three econometricians, Lawrence Klein, Daniel Suits, and Arthur S. Goldberger, have built a 25-equation model of the U.S. economy.[1]

They do not look on their model as a once-and-for-all job, but are continuously testing and strengthening it. When a forecast turns out to be off the mark, the Michigan group probes into the machinery of the model to find out just where the fault lies, changes the model to try to correct the mistake next time. And to make the model more realistic, the group is also making intensive studies of particular sectors of the economy, including the construction industry, foreign trade, agriculture, and the money market.

Industry's own economists are beginning to get into the model-building field. For industry's purposes the models have been simplified. Management has found them useful for doing one of the principal jobs for which business is turning to economists:

1. [For a more recent model, see J. Duesenberry, G. Fromm, L. Klein, and E. Kuh, *The Brookings Quarterly Econometric Model of the U.S. Economy* (North Holland, 1965). *Editor*]

helping guide planning for capital spending and expansion programs by producing long-range projections of specific industries' places in the national economy.

Some industry economists say the models provide the best technique yet developed for organizing massive and complex statistical data, for cumulating knowledge and profiting from past errors and successes, and for systematizing the whole forecasting process.

Economics and Business Planning

SIDNEY S. ALEXANDER

Sidney Alexander is Professor of Industrial Management at the Massachusetts Institute of Technology. This article is taken from his contribution to Economics and the Policy Maker, *published in 1959.*

While the most obvious task of the economist in the large corporation is short-run forecasting, his most valuable contribution, it seems to me, is in long-run planning. To some extent, this is a consequence of the greater amenability of long-run developments to economic forecasting techniques. While it is often quite hard to estimate whether the fourth quarter of next year will have a gross national product higher or lower than the fourth quarter of this year, it can quite reliably be estimated that the gross national product ten years from now will be some 35 percent higher than it was this year. More precisely, it can be estimated that the long-term trend value that economic historians will come to assign to 1969 will be some 35 percent greater than the long-term trend value they will come to assign to 1959.

The major contribution that an economic mode of thought in particular, or a scientific mode of thought in general, can make to the analysis of business problems, and those of government too, is the reduction of the problems to rational study, the transfer of as much as possible out of the field of the intuitively and implicitly appraised to that of the rationally and explicitly appraised.

The best consultants I know are uniform in their agreement that they contribute to their clients little more than applied common sense. But why can applied common sense be a contribution? Essentially because in attacking the problem the first task is to recognize the problem explicitly, and this is not habitually done by an active type. No discredit is implied here; the contemplative type is probably not very good at making and executing decisions. We should not be surprised that in this activity as in others, productivity can be increased by the division of labor, provided, as always, the extent of the market will support the division of labor. One man can profitably specialize in running a business and meeting its day-to-day problems and another in studying those factors that are likely to affect the business in the long run. Different skills and temperaments are suited to each of these activities.

Many of the critical decisions of long-run planning are once-in-a-decade decisions, some are once in a lifetime. It can hardly be expected that anyone could handle such problems on the basis of his own personal experience. There should be no wonder that this sort of analysis is a field for specialization. Those skills most important for the businessman—skills in negotiation, in execution, and in administration—are not usually associated with the sort of introspective analysis appropriate for the projection into an "as if" world of the future. But the economist is a specialist in the analysis of the "as if." As one Brookings author has stated, "Economic analysis is a substitute for the sixth sense of businessmen." The sixth sense probably does better in sensing the short-run situation, but not as well in sensing the long-run. Even when the businessman himself would be highly skilled at making such a study, the doctrine of comparative advantage suggests that it may be more advantageous to turn the study over to a specialist in analysis while the businessman concentrates on problems of administration and execution.

The characteristic long-run problem of the business enterprise is what business should it be in and on what scale. This is the principal content of business planning, and it centers on capital budgeting.

Long-range planning, or LRP, as it is frequently referred to, is now a big word in business. The devotees of LRP speak of its advantages much as the old line socialists spoke of society under socialism—when everything will be better. "Fuzzy management disappears when LRP is applied." "Crisis management becomes less pronounced." "Short-term dips assume less significance." "New markets are entered as soon as possible." "Money and men come easier." "Long-range planning . . . is a mark of industrial leadership by which good management is made more effective and good companies retain or attain recognition in their industry." These statements, taken out of their context of a discussion of long-range planning in a management journal, possibly give an oversimplified picture of the enthusiasm for long-range planning on the part of its advocates, but they do not exaggerate the intensity of that enthusiasm.

Clearly, planning can confer such benefits only if it is good planning. Most of the literature on planning in business is aimed at the form rather than the substance of planning. Implicit in this is the idea that even a poor plan is better than none at all, since the planning process is unlikely to result in a worse outcome than unplanned behavior. And there is probably some truth in this. Because the very act of planning does require explicit consideration of the relevant factors, it is less likely that an important consideration will be ignored. But most of the literature stops short of the substantive problem of how, in fact, the future is to be projected as the basic assumption for the long-range plans. That is the great opportunity for the economist.

The economist can make a valuable contribution to the solution of long-run business problems because his mode of thought, based on microeconomics and descriptive economics, is particularly attuned to the analysis of the long run, and because his role of outsider affords a broader perspective and leads to explicit examination of practices that would otherwise be taken for granted. Any scientifically trained person would share many of these characteristics, but the economist has the further advantage of familiarity with the class of problems encountered in business and with the data and the techniques of empirical research appropriate to this class of problems.

Parkinson's Law

C. Northcote Parkinson

*C. Northcote Parkinson is Raffles Professor
of History at the University of Singapore.
This article first appeared in the* Economist
in November 1955.

It is a commonplace observation that work expands so as to fill the time available for its completion. Thus, an elderly lady of leisure can spend an entire day in writing and dispatching a postcard to her niece at Bognor Regis. An hour will be spent in finding the postcard, another in hunting for spectacles, half-an-hour in a search for the address, an hour and a quarter in composition, and twenty minutes in deciding whether or not to take an umbrella when going to the pillar-box in the next street. The total effort which would occupy a busy man for three minutes all told may in this fashion leave another person prostrate after a day of doubt, anxiety and toil.

Granted that work (and especially paper work) is thus elastic in its demands on time, it is manifest that there need be little or no relationship between the work to be done and the size of the staff to which it may be assigned. Before the discovery of a new scientific law—herewith presented to the public for the first time, and to be called Parkinson's Law[1]—there has, however, been insufficient recognition of the implication of this fact in the field of public administration. Politicians and taxpayers have assumed

1. Why? Why not?—Editor.

(with occasional phases of doubt) that a rising total in the number of civil servants must reflect a growing volume of work to be done. Cynics, in questioning this belief, have imagined that the multiplication of officials must have left some of them idle or all of them able to work for shorter hours. But this is a matter in which faith and doubt seem equally misplaced. The fact is that the number of the officials and the quantity of the work to be done are not related to each other at all. The rise in the total of those employed is governed by Parkinson's Law, and would be much the same whether the volume of the work were to increase, diminish or even disappear. The importance of Parkinson's Law lies in the fact that it is a law of growth based upon an analysis of the factors by which the growth is controlled.

The validity of this recently discovered law must rely mainly on statistical proofs, which will follow. Of more interest to the general reader is the explanation of the factors that underlie the general tendency to which this law gives definition. Omitting technicalities (which are numerous) we may distinguish, at the outset, two motive forces. They can be represented for the present purpose by two almost axiomatic statements, thus:

Factor I. An official wants to multiply subordinates, not rivals; and

Factor II. Officials make work for each other. We must now examine these motive forces in turn.

THE LAW OF MULTIPLICATION OF SUBORDINATES

To comprehend Factor I, we must picture a civil servant called A who finds himself overworked. Whether this overwork is real or imaginary is immaterial; but we should observe, in passing, that A's sensation (or illusion) might easily result from his own decreasing energy—a normal symptom of middle-age. For this real or imagined overwork there are, broadly speaking, three possible remedies:

(1) He may resign.
(2) He may ask to halve the work with a colleague called B.
(3) He may demand the assistance of two subordinates to be called C and D.

There is probably no instance in civil service history of A choos-

ing any but the third alternative. By resignation he would lose
his pension rights. By having *B* appointed, on his own level in
the hierarchy, he would merely bring in a rival for promotion to
W's vacancy when *W* (at long last) retires. So *A* would rather
have *C* and *D*, junior men, below him. They will add to his
consequence; and, by dividing the work into two categories, as
between *C* and *D*, he will have the merit of being the only man
who comprehends them both.

It is essential to realize, at this point, that *C* and *D* are, as it
were, inseparable. To appoint *C* alone would have been impossible. Why? Because *C*, if by himself, would divide the work with
A and so assume almost the equal status which has been refused
in the first instance to *B*; a status the more emphasized if *C* is *A*'s
only possible successor. Subordinates must thus number two or
more, each being kept in order by fear of the other's promotion.
When *C* complains in turn of being overworked (as he certainly
will) *A* will, with the concurrence of *C*, advise the appointment
of two assistants to help *C*. But he can then avert internal friction
only by advising the appointment of two more assistants to help
D, whose position is much the same. With this recruitment of *E*,
F, *G* and *H*, the promotion of *A* is now practically certain.

THE LAW OF MULTIPLICATION OF WORK

Seven officials are now doing what one did before. This is
where Factor II comes into operation. For these seven make so
much work for each other that all are fully occupied and *A* is
actually working harder than ever. An incoming document may
well come before each of them in turn. Official *E* decides that it
falls within the province of *F*, who places a draft reply before *C*,
who amends it drastically before consulting *D*, who asks *G* to
deal with it. But *G* goes on leave at this point, handing the file
over to *H*, who drafts a minute, which is signed by *D* and returned
to *C*, who revises his draft accordingly and lays the new version
before *A*.

What does *A* do? He would have every excuse for signing the
thing unread, for he has many other matters on his mind. Knowing now that he is to succeed *W* next year, he has to decide
whether *C* or *D* should succeed to his own office. He had to

agree to G going on leave, although not yet strictly entitled to it. He is worried whether H should not have gone instead, for reasons of health. He has looked pale recently—partly but not solely because of his domestic troubles. Then there is the business of F's special increment of salary for the period of the conference, and E's application for transfer to the Ministry of Pensions. A has heard that D is in love with a married typist and that G and F are no longer on speaking terms—no one seems to know why. So A might be tempted to sign C's draft and have done with it.

But A is a conscientious man. Beset as he is with problems created by his colleagues for themselves and for him—created by the mere fact of these officials' existence—he is not the man to shirk his duty. He reads through the draft with care, deletes the fussy paragraphs added by C and H and restores the thing back to the form preferred in the first instance by the able (if quarrelsome) F. He corrects the English—none of these young men can write grammatically—and finally produces the same reply he would have written if officials C to H had never been born. Far more people have taken far longer to produce the same result. No one has been idle. All have done their best. And it is late in the evening before A finally quits his office and begins the return journey to Ealing. The last of the office lights are being turned off in the gathering dusk which marks the end of another day's administrative toil. Among the last to leave, A reflects, with bowed shoulders and a wry smile, that late hours, like grey hairs, are among the penalties of success.

THE SCIENTIFIC PROOFS

From this description of the factors at work the student of political science will recognize that administrators are more or less bound to multiply. Nothing has yet been said, however, about the period of time likely to elapse between the date of A's appointment and the date from which we can calculate the pensionable service of H. Vast masses of statistical evidence have been collected and it is from a study of this data that Parkinson's Law has been deduced. Space will not allow of detailed analysis, but research began in the British Navy Estimates.

These were chosen because the Admiralty's responsibilities are more easily measurable than those of (say) the Board of Trade.

The accompanying table is derived from Admiralty statistics for 1914 and 1928. The criticism voiced at the time centered on the comparison between the sharp fall in numbers of those available for fighting and the sharp rise in those available only for administration, the creation, it was said, of "a magnificent Navy on land." But that comparison is not to the present purpose. What we have to note is that the 2,000 Admiralty officials of 1914 had become the 3,569 of 1928; and that this growth was unrelated to any possible increase in their work. The Navy during that period had diminished, in point of fact, by a third in men and two-thirds in ships. Nor, from 1922 onwards, was its strength even expected to increase, for its total of ships (unlike its total of officials) was limited by the Washington Naval Agreement of that year. Yet in these circumstances we had a 78.45 percent increase in Admiralty officials over a period of fourteen years; an average increase of 5.6 percent a year on the earlier total. In fact, as we shall see, the rate of increase was not as regular as that. All we have to consider, at this stage, is the percentage rise over a given period.

ADMIRALTY STATISTICS

	1914	1928	Percentage increase or decrease
Capital ships in commission	62	20	—67.74
Officers and men in Royal Navy	146,000	100,000	—31.50
Dockyard workers	57,000	62,439	+ 9.54
Dockyard officials and clerks	3,249	4,558	+40.28
Admiralty officials	2,000	3,569	+78.45

Can this rise in the total number of civil servants be accounted for except on the assumption that such a total must always rise by a law governing its growth? It might be urged, at this point, that the period under discussion was one of rapid development in naval technique. The use of the flying machine was no longer confined to the eccentric. Submarines were tolerated if not approved. Engineer officers were beginning to be regarded as almost human. In so revolutionary an age we might expect the storekeepers would have more elaborate inventories to compile. We might not wonder to see more draughtsmen on the payroll, more designers, more technicians and scientists. But these, the dockyard officials, increased only by 40 percent in number, while the men of Whitehall increased by nearly 80 percent. For every new foreman or electrical engineer at Portsmouth there had to be two or more clerks at Charing Cross. From this we might be tempted to conclude, provisionally, that the rate of increase in administrative staff is likely to be double that of the technical staff at a time when the actually useful strength (in this case, of seamen) is being reduced by 31.5 percent. It has been proved, however, statistically, that this last percentage is irrelevant. *The Officials would have multiplied at the same rate had there been no actual seamen at all.*

It would be interesting to follow the further progress by which the 8,118 Admiralty staff of 1935 came to number 33,788 by 1954. But the staff of the Colonial Office affords a better field of study during a period of Imperial decline. The relevant statistics are set down below. Before showing what the rate of increase is, we must observe that the extent of this department's responsibilities was far from constant during these twenty years. The colonial territories were not much altered in area or population between 1935 and 1939. They were considerably diminished by 1943, certain areas being in enemy hands. They were increased again in 1947, but have since then shrunk steadily from year to year as successive colonies achieve self-government.

COLONIAL OFFICE OFFICIALS

1935	1939	1943	1947	1954
372	450	817	1,139	1,661

It would be rational, prior to the discovery of Parkinson's Law, to suppose that these changes in the scope of Empire would be reflected in the size of its central administration. But a glance at the figures shows that the staff totals represent automatic stages in an inevitable increase. And this increase, while related to that observed in other departments, has nothing to do with the size— or even the existence—of the Empire. What are the percentages

of increase? We must ignore, for this purpose, the rapid increase
in staff which accompanied the diminution of responsibility
during World War II. We should note rather the peacetime rates
of increase over 5.24 percent between 1935 and 1939, and 6.55
percent between 1947 and 1954. This gives an average increase
of 5.89 percent each year, a percentage markedly similar to that
already found in the Admiralty staff increase between 1914 and
1928.

Further and detailed statistical analysis of departmental staffs
would be inappropriate in such an article as this. It is hoped,
however, to reach a tentative conclusion regarding the time likely
to elapse between a given official's first appointment and the
later appointment of his two or more assistants. Dealing with
the problem of pure staff accumulation, all the researches so far
completed point to an average increase of about 5¾ percent per
year. This fact established, it now becomes possible to state
Parkinson's Law in mathematical form, thus:

In any public administrative department not actually at war
the staff increase may be expected to follow this formula:

$$x = \frac{2k^m + p}{n}$$

where k is the number of staff seeking promotion through the
appointment of subordinates; p represents the difference between
the ages of appointment and retirement; m is the number of man-
hours devoted to answering minutes within the department; and
n is the number of effective units being administered. Then x
will be the number of new staff required each year.

Mathematicians will, of course, realize that to find the percentage increase they must multiply x by 100 and divide by the
total of the previous year, thus:

$$\frac{100 \, (2k^m + p)}{yn} \%$$

where y represents the total original staff. And this figure will
invariably prove to be between 5.17 percent and 6.56 percent,
irrespective of any variation in the amount of work (if any) to be
done.

The discovery of this formula and of the general principles upon which it is based has, of course, no emotive value. No attempt has been made to inquire whether departments ought to grow in size. Those who hold that this growth is essential to gain full employment are fully entitled to their opinion. Those who doubt the stability of an economy based upon reading each other's minutes are equally entitled to theirs. Parkinson's Law is a purely scientific discovery, inapplicable except in theory to the politics of the day. It is not the business of the botanist to eradicate the weeds. Enough for him if he can tell us just how fast they grow.

Part Three

Operations Research: An Introduction to Selected Techniques

THE essays in Part Three provide an introduction to the nature, purpose, and usefulness of various concepts and techniques in operations research. They do not delve into technical details but concentrate instead on those aspects of operations research which a general manager would find useful.

The first two papers are concerned with the nature of operations research. Cyril Herrmann and John Magee attempt to define operations research and to describe the ways in which it has been applied to business problems. They identify and discuss four concepts of fundamental importance to the practice of operations research: the model, the measure of effectiveness, the necessity for decision, and the role of experimentation. The second article, from *Fortune*, describes some of the techniques used by operations researchers: mathematical programming, game theory, statistical decision theory, scheduling techniques, and dynamic programming.

The next three papers are concerned with mathematical programming, one of the most important of these techniques. Alexander Henderson and Robert Schlaifer describe how the H. J. Heinz Company used mathematical programming to determine the level of production in various plants as well as the pattern of shipments from plants to warehouses. George Dantzig discusses the basic concepts involved in linear programming and describes the sorts of problems that this technique can handle. To be a linear programming model, Dantzig explains, a system must satisfy certain assumptions of proportionality, nonnegativity, and additivity. Using graphical techniques, Robert Dorfman presents a very simple example of mathematical programming.

The following four papers deal with the theory of games and decision-making under uncertainty. John McDonald discusses one-person, two-person, and three-person games, using the liquor industry to illustrate a two-person game and various cases of industrial combination to illustrate games with more than two persons. J. D. Williams shows how conflict situations must be described in order to be amenable to game-theory analysis; the basic elements are the number of persons, the payoff, the strategy, and the game matrix. Martin Shubik discusses briefly some alternative theories of decision-making under uncertainty. John Pratt, Howard Raiffa, and Robert Schlaifer take up decision trees and present elements of modern statistical decision theory.

The last two papers are an introduction to inventory and queuing theory. The short piece by Thomson M. Whitin introduces the reader to the lot-size formula used to calculate economical purchase quantities. As Whitin points out, this formula is by no means new. William Baumol describes the salient characteristics of queuing problems, which have received a great deal of attention from operations researchers, and shows how Monte Carlo techniques can be used to solve them.

Operations Research

CYRIL HERRMANN AND JOHN MAGEE

This article appeared in the Harvard Business Review, August 1953. At that time Cyril Herrmann was a faculty member at Massachusetts Institute of Technology and John Magee was on the staff of Arthur D. Little, Inc.

Operations research has helped companies to solve such diverse business problems as directing salesmen to the right accounts at the right time, dividing the advertising budget in the most effective way, establishing equitable bonus systems, improving inventory and reordering policies, planning minimum-cost production schedules, and estimating the amount of clerical help needed for a new operation.

Operations research makes possible accomplishments like these and many others because (a) it helps to single out the critical issues which require executive appraisal and analysis, and (b) it provides factual bases to support and guide executive judgment. Thus, it eases the burden of effort and time on executives but intensifies the potential of their decision-making role. In this sense operations research contributes toward better management.

ESSENTIAL FEATURES OF OPERATIONS RESEARCH

Operations research apparently means different things to different people. To some businessmen and scientists it means only the application of statistics and common sense to business problems. Indeed, one vice president of a leading company remarked that if his division heads did not practice it every day, they would not last long. To others it is just another and perhaps more comprehensive term for existing activities like market research, quality control, or industrial engineering. Some businessmen consider it a new sales or production gimmick; some, a product of academic people interfering in the practical world. In truth, operations research is none of these things.

It should not be surprising that there has been this confusion. Operations research is not an explicit, easily identifiable concept that developed to meet the specific needs of industry. It was first applied in World War II by groups of scientists who were engaged by the government to help frame recommendations for the improvement of military activities. After the war a few soundly managed companies experimented with it and found that it worked successfully in business operations as well; and it has since gained a secure foothold in industry.

Early attempts by operations analysts to describe their activities, based on the objective of arriving at a precise and comprehensive definition of operations research, tended to be overly generalized, broad, and self-conscious, and suffered from emphasis on military applications. Some of the confusion surrounding the meaning of the term "operations research" has resulted from attempts at identification with special techniques or unnecessarily rigid distinctions between operations research and other management service activities.

Now, let us see if we can cut through some of this confusion.

The first point to grasp is that operations research is what its name implies, research on operations. However, it involves a particular view of operations and, even more important, a particular kind of research.

Operations are considered as an entity. The subject matter studied is not the equipment used, nor the morale of the participants, nor the physical properties of the output; it is the combination of these in total, as an economic process. And operations so conceived are subject to analysis by the mental processes and the methodologies which we have come to associate with the research work of the physicist, the chemist, and the biologist—what has come to be called "the scientific method."

The basic premise underlying the scientific method is a simple and abiding faith in the rationality of nature, leading to the belief that phenomena have a cause. If phenomena do have a cause, it is the scientists' contention that by hard work the mechanism or system underlying the observed facts can be discovered. Once the mechanism is known, nature's secrets are known and can be used to the investigator's own best advantage.

The scientist knows that his analogue to nature will never be perfect. But it must be sufficiently accurate to suit the particular purposes at hand; and, until it is, he must repeat the processes of observation, induction, and theory construction—again and again. Note that a satisfactory solution must be in quantitative terms in order that it can be predictive—the only accepted fundamental test of being physically meaningful.

The scientific method, in its ideal form, calls for a rather special mental attitude, foremost in which is a reverence for facts. Of course all modern executives are accustomed to using figures to control their operations. But they are primarily concerned with results and only secondarily with causes; they interpret their facts in the light of company objectives. This is a much different attitude from seeking out the relationships underlying the facts.

Thus, when an executive looks at sales figures, he looks at them primarily in terms of the success of his sales campaign and its effect on profits. By contrast, when the scientist looks at these same figures, he seeks in them a clue to the fundamental behavior pattern of the customers. By the process of induction he tentatively formulates a theoretical system or mechanism; then by the inverse process of deduction he determines what phenomena should take place and checks these against the observed facts. His test is simple: Does the assumed mechanism act enough like nature—or, more specifically in this case, does it produce quantitative data such as can be used for predicting how the customers will in fact behave?

Through the years mathematical and experimental techniques have been developed to implement this attitude. The application of the scientific attitude and the associated techniques to the study of operations, whether business, governmental, or military, is what is meant by operations research.

Newton was able to explain the apparently totally unrelated phenomena of planetary motion and objects falling on the earth by the simple unifying concept of gravity. This represented a tremendous step forward in helping men to understand and control the world about them. Again, more recently, the power of the scientific method was demonstrated by the ability of the nuclear physicists to predict the tremendous energy potential lying within the atom.

Here are a few summary examples of the way this same kind of approach has been applied to down-to-earth business problems.

A company with a number of products made at three different locations was concerned about the items to be produced at each location and the points at which the items would be warehoused. Freight costs constituted a substantial part of the delivered cost of the material. Operations research showed that what appeared to be a complex and involved problem could be broken into a series of rather simple components. Adaptations of linear programing methods were used to find the warehousing schedule which would minimize freight costs. The study is now being extended to determine the best distribution of products among manufacturing plants and warehouse locations in order to minimize net delivered cost in relation to return on investment.

A manufacturer of chemical products, with a wide and varied line, sought more rational or logical bases than the customary percentage of sales for distributing his limited advertising budget among products, some of which were growing, some stable, and others declining. An operations research study showed that advertising effectiveness was related to three simple characteristics, each of which could be estimated from existing sales data with satisfactory reliability: (*a*) the total market potential; (*b*) the rate of growth of sales; (*c*) the customer loss rate. A mathematical formulation of these three characteristics provided a rational basis for distributing advertising and promotional effort.

In a company making a line of light machines, the executive board questioned the amount of money spent for missionary salesmen calling on customers. Studies yielded explicit mathematical statements of (*a*) the relation between the number of accounts called on and resulting sales volume and (*b*) the relation between sales costs and manufacturing and distribution costs. These were combined by the methods of differential calculus to set up simple tables for picking the level of promotion in each area which would maximize company net profits. The results showed that nearly a 50 per cent increase in promotional activity was economically feasible and would yield substantial profits.

An industrial products manufacturer wanted to set time standards as a basis for costs and labor efficiency controls. The operations research group studied several complex operations; expressed the effect of the physical characteristics of products and equipment and the time required to produce a given amount of output in the form of mathematical equations; and then, without further extensive time study or special data collection, set up tables of production time standards according to product characteristics, equipment used, and worker efficiency, which could be applied to any or all of the production operations.

A company carrying an inventory of a large number of finished items had trouble maintaining sound and balanced stock levels. Despite careful attention and continued modification of reorder points in the light of experience, the stock of many individual items turned out to be either too high for sales or inadequate to meet demand. The problem was solved by a physical chemist who first collected data on the variables, such as size and frequency of order, length of production and delivery time, etc.; then set up an assumed system, which he tried out against extreme sales situations, continually changing its characteristics slightly until it met the necessary conditions—all on paper (a technique well known to physical scientists); and thus was able to determine a workable system without cost of installation and risk of possible failure.

These examples should serve to give some idea of how the scientific method can be applied. But they represent only a few of the many scientific techniques available (as we shall see when we examine further cases in more detail). Some practitioners even take the rather broad point of view that operations research should include the rather indefinite and qualitative methods of the social science fields. Most professional opinion, however, favors the view that operations research is more restricted in meaning, limited to the quantitative methods and experimentally verifiable results of the physical sciences.

BASIC CONCEPTS OF OPERATIONS RESEARCH

There are four concepts of fundamental importance to the practice of operations research: (*a*) the model, (*b*) the measure of effectiveness, (*c*) the necessity for decision, and (*d*) the role of experimentation.

The most frequently encountered concept in operations research is that of the model—the simplified representation of an operation, containing only those aspects which are of primary importance to the problem under study. It has been of great use in facilitating the investigation of operations. To illustrate with some familiar types of "models" from other fields:

(1) In aeronautical engineering the model of an aeroplane is used to investigate its aerodynamic properties in a wind tunnel. While perfectly adequate for this purpose, it would hardly do for practical use. It has no seats; it may not even be hollow. It is, however, a satisfactory physical model for studying the flight characteristics of the ship.

(2) Another, quite different kind of model is the accounting model. This is essentially a simplified representation on paper, in the form of accounts and ledgers, of the flow of goods and services through a business enterprise. It provides measures of the rate of flow, the values produced, and the performances achieved, and to that extent is useful (though it is hardly a realistic representation of operations).

(3) Many models are used in physics. Three-dimensional models of complex molecules are probably most familiar to laymen, but the most powerful models in this field are sets of mathematical equations.

There are several different types of operations research models. Most of them are mathematical in form, being a set of equations relating significant variables in the operation to the outcome.

Related to the concept of a model or theory of operation is the measure of effectiveness, whereby the extent to which the operation is attaining its goal can be explicitly determined. One common over-all measure of effectiveness in industrial operations is return on investment; another is net dollar profit. Measures of effectiveness down the scale might be the number of customers serviced per hour, the ratio of productive to total hours of a machine operation, etc.

A consistent statement of the fundamental goals of the operation is essential to the mathematical logic of the model. (It does not matter if the goals are complex.) Just as the model cannot make two and two add up to five, so it is impossible to relate fundamentally inconsistent objectives and produce consistent and meaningful results.

Operations research has frequently brought to light inconsistencies in company goals. Take production scheduling, for instance. Very often its object has been stated as scheduling production to meet sales forecasts with minimum production costs, with minimum inventory investment, and without customer-service failure. Yet minimizing inventory investment typically requires the use of start-and-stop or at best uneven production plans, resulting in excessive production costs; and eliminating the risk of not being able to ship every customer order immediately requires huge inventories, in the face of fluctuating and at least partially unpredictable demand. The solution is to combine and sublimate such otherwise inconsistent goals to a higher unified and consistent goal.

The statement of a complete and wholly consistent goal of company operations must be recognized as an ideal. Business goals are very complex, and to catch the full flavor of the objectives of an intricate business operation in any simple, explicit statement is difficult. Many business goals remain, and probably ever will remain, at least in part intangible—e.g., efforts to improve employee morale or contribute to the public welfare. To that extent, the objective of operations research must be more modest than the construction of a complete model and the measurement of the extent to which the operation is attaining the complete set of goals established for it. But it still can serve to clarify the interdependency of those intangibles with the company goals which in fact are measurable, thus providing a guide to executive decision.

The third concept inherent in operations research is that of decision and decision making. An essential element in all true operations research problems is the existence of alternative courses of action, with a choice to be made among them; otherwise the study of an operation becomes academic or theoretical. This should be clear from the cases already cited.

In sum, the objective of operations research is to clarify the relation between the several courses of action, determine their outcomes, and indicate which measures up best in terms of the company goal. But note that, while this should be of assistance to the executive in making his decision intelligently, in every case the ultimate responsibility still lies with him.

The fourth significant concept concerns the role of experimentation. Operations research is the application of experimental science to the study of operations. The theory, or model, is generally built up from observed data or experience, although in some cases the model development may depend heavily on external or a priori information. In any event, the theory describing the operation must always be verifiable experimentally. Two kinds of experiments are important in this connection:

(1) The first kind is designed simply to get information. Thus, it often takes the form of an apparently rather impractical test. In one case the operations analysts directed advertising toward potential customers the company knew were not worth addressing, and refrained from addressing customers the company typically sought—and for a very simple reason. There was plenty of evidence indicating what happened when advertising was directed toward those normally addressed but not enough about its effects upon those not normally addressed. To evaluate the effectiveness of the advertising, therefore, it was necessary to find out what happened to those normally promoted when they were not promoted, and what happened to those normally not promoted when they were.

(2) The other type of experiment is the critical type; it is designed to test the validity of conclusions. Again, what appear to be rather impractical forms of experimentation are sometimes used. Thus, in the most sensitive experiments of this type, the validity of the theory or model can often be tested most revealingly in terms of the results of extreme policies rather than in terms of the more normal policy likely to be put into practice.

Decision Theory and Program Scheduling

Fortune MAGAZINE

The author, George A. W. Boehm, is an associate editor of Fortune; *this article appeared in the April 1962 issue.*

Throughout history men have employed elaborate rituals for making up their minds. They have poured libations and sacrificed oxen in hopes of persuading a capricious and possibly hostile Nature to reward their decisions. They have consulted sibyls and watched the flight of birds to discover what the future holds in store. They have put their faith in proverbs and rules of thumb devised to take some of the guesswork out of living. They have sought divine guidance, as did George Romney, former president of American Motors, when he fasted and meditated before deciding to seek the Republican nomination for governor of Michigan.

In managing the affairs of modern business and government more scientific decision methods are needed. Unaided, the human mind cannot possibly weigh the manifold complexities involved in the development of a missile, the erection of a forty-story office building, the operation of an enterprise producing hundreds of products for millions of customers. Thousands of decisions go into scheduling jobs, ordering supplies, managing inventories, negotiating with contractors, hiring labor, pricing goods, and planning production facilities. The executive is further harassed by such uncertainties as the unpredictable tastes of consumers and the speculative nature of economic forecasts and research and development programs. Thus all too often he must act largely on hunch and intuition—and go home with the gnawing suspicion that he might have decided more wisely.

In recent years scientists have been showing the executive how to avoid some of the perplexity that attends decision making. They have been putting together a voluminous bundle of mathematical techniques for evaluating possible courses of action. In attempting to rationalize the process of deciding, they have developed "decision theory." This is not really a single theory of how to make decisions, but rather a collection of techniques for weighing many factors in logical fashion. Some of the techniques are best suited to situations in which, though all the factors are known or predictable, the complexity is so confusing that the human mind cannot arrive at a wholly rational decision. Other techniques cope with "risks"—chances that can be accurately measured or calculated, such as the probability that a given number of insurance policyholders will die within a year. Still others deal with "uncertainties" (which scientists carefully distinguish from "risks")—chances that can be estimated only roughly at best, because, for example, they depend on future developments or the behavior of a competitor. All decision theory, however, has a common purpose: to show decision makers surer ways to attain their goals.

Decision theorists use some tools that were developed several decades ago, notably statistical sampling, and some that are less familiar, such as linear programing, a short-cut method of finding the best way to allocate scarce resources. In addition, some brand-new techniques are being perfected. Two of the most successful, PERT and CPM (which will be explained later), are now used to schedule most United States space programs and many large construction jobs. To date, the various kinds of mathematical decision aids have been effectively applied to controlling inventory levels, arranging bus schedules, planning preventive maintenance, determining the best operating conditions for oil refineries, and scheduling many other industrial and military logistic operations that depend on the making of many routine but intricately related decisions.

Decision theory caught on first in the petroleum industry, which has a tradition of exploiting scientific techniques to control its production and marketing procedures. Other research-minded enterprises, including most of the big chemical and electrical firms, are now also making wide use of decision theory, and a few other industries are beginning to adopt it.

The techniques are too complicated to be applied by amateurs; the executive must call upon a specialist. Many big companies have staffs of decision experts, who are usually designated by some other name—e.g., planning, applied mathematics, or operations research. The executive without such a staff can turn to any of more than a score of consultants, many of whom specialize in industrial production, economic planning, or some other field of decision making. The Air Force has its own group of decision-theory consultants—the Rand Corporation. Serving private industry are a number of consulting firms that are capable of inventing new decision techniques for special applications.

Any group of decision experts is likely to include men with varied backgrounds, for the theoretical ideas stem from a wide range of scientific disciplines: mathematics, physics, systems engineering, econometrics, statistics, and servomechanism theory, which originally applied to automatic controls. But whatever his approach, the decision theorist must understand how to use computers. The techniques usually demand a prodigious amount of calculation. To apply them on large-scale problems without a computer would be as unthinkable as to work out a complex engineering design with Roman numerals.

The new scientific approach might suggest the possibility that even the most far-reaching business decisions could be turned over entirely to computers. But executives have no reason to fear that they will be replaced by machines producing decisions "untouched by human brains." Hunch and intuition are still invaluable. Indeed, most decision theorists today are looking for ways to incorporate expert judgment with their mathematics. They want to take full advantage of the comprehensiveness of the human mind to augment the precision of computers. For his part, the executive of the future will depend on the tools of decision theory much as an airplane pilot relies on his instruments. If he can learn to understand the theory well enough to appraise its applications, he can free himself from many routine responsibilities and broaden the scope of his thinking.

This inclusion of judgment is making decision theory more realistic, but at the same time it may cost the theory some of its mathematical incisiveness. Some leaders in the field used to cherish the somewhat arrogant hope that pure mathematics might produce perfectly precise and automatic decisions. Now they are aware that decision theory will be used less to dictate optimal courses of action, more to present the human decision maker with a choice of feasible actions and help him choose a good one.

The marriage of judgment to mathematics requires considerable ingenuity. Not infrequently the decision theorist must be a virtuoso psychologist in order to translate intuition and opinions into the numbers and mathematical functions that a computer can process. People tend to think about their jobs in one way, describe them in another, and actually perform them in a third way. For example, the warehouse manager who claims he has never been late on a promised delivery date may be talking quite frankly; but perhaps he has achieved his remarkable record by setting back the date whenever he has foreseen a jam. He may also find it difficult to assess the value of some quite ordinary factors—e.g., how much an inventory shortage might cost his company in lost sales and irate customers. He might be able, however, to estimate the cost indirectly in different terms, such as the amount he would be willing to spend for air freight in an emergency.

Far knottier problems arise because people are often erratic and inarticulate when they try to explain what they want to accomplish. Theoretical economists conceive of a marvelously rational being whom they call "economic man": he has a clear idea of what ends he wants to attain, and, given alternatives, he has the wisdom to calculate which one will be most rewarding in terms of his personal scale of values. But the very fact that personal values are part of the equation casts doubt on whether there can ever be an authentic "economic man." One of the most valuable services a decision theorist can perform is to list alternative courses of action and spell out the risks and payoffs associated with each. But if he is actually going to recommend an acceptable decision, he may first have to determine his client's attitude toward taking chances, which is an element in the client's personal scale of values. Several gambling strategies have been formulated mathematically so that they can be incorporated in some decision methods. For the pessimist who regards himself as an underdog faced by hostile Nature, there is the "minimax" strategy. This guides him to choose the course of action that entails the minimum risk of disaster, although it may also reduce his chance of winning. Against a wise and powerful adversary, "minimax" is clearly the prudent policy. For the unbridled optimist who likes to plunge on long shots, this is "maximax." This enables him to shoot for big gains although he runs a big risk of large loss. And for the patient man who regards life as an unending series of gambles and expects his luck to average out, there is the "maximum expected value" strategy. Given about an even number of good and bad breaks, this will maximize his chances of profiting in the long run.

Interest in decision theory is now booming, thanks largely to the striking success of two new scheduling procedures: Critical Path Method (CPM) and Program Evaluation and Review Technique (PERT), which differ from each other only in a few details. They enable managers to keep tight control of the timing and budgets of even the most complex and widely scattered projects. Scheduling of such programs actually consists of a multitude of interrelated decisions—e.g., when to promise delivery, how many electricians to hire for a given week, when to order materials and how to ship them, which contractor to employ. The new procedures are relatively simple to apply and interpret. Yet they produce many decisions almost automatically, while giving the manager wide scope to use his judgment and without burdening him with mathematical details.

In both CPM and PERT, the first step is to analyze all the work that must be done, break it down into individual tasks, and then estimate how long each will probably take and how much it will cost. This information is then diagramed as a network showing what activities must await the completion of other jobs and what work can be carried on in parallel with other phases of the project.

The scheduling network is based on the obvious logic that people commonly apply to any number of everyday activities. For example, a methodical hostess planning a party might make a list including all that will have to be done: order meat and vegetables, bake a cake, polish the silver, hire a maid, buy liquor, buy a new dress, get a permanent, set up a bar, set the table, etc. And she will have a good idea of the timing of every item on the list. Similarly, most able industrial managers presumably have kept in the backs of their minds at least a vague idea of a job network. But until the advent of electronic computers, it would have been futile actually to draw detailed networks. Projects large enough to require elaborate planning are usually represented by networks that are far too complicated for the unaided human mind to analyze and adjust—over 1,000 steps for the construction of a modest industrial plant, up to perhaps 30,000 for the development of a large missile.

A modern computer, however, can derive all sorts of useful information from the network. All the time and cost estimates and the relation of every job to all the others are reduced to a numerically coded program. Then, in a matter of minutes, the computer can calculate how long the project will take and how much it will cost. The over-all time estimate depends on a key concept: the "critical path." This is a sequence of jobs in which any slowdown will delay the completion of the entire project. Conversely, if these jobs are rushed, the whole project will be completed earlier. Generally, most jobs do not lie along the critical path; if they take a little longer than expected, the project will still finish on time. In principle, a human being could apply this concept just as a computer does, and take steps to shorten the time along the critical path. But it might take him days, even weeks, to find just which path is critical. The computer also does what no human mind could possibly accomplish: it shows continually how plans should be changed to keep the project on schedule and within the budget. Users of network scheduling avoid costly over-all crash programs; they have found that even in emergencies they seldom have to expedite more than ten per cent of the work. Besides, they don't have to waste time in tedious coordinating conferences.

The inventors of CPM and PERT started with somewhat different objectives but wound up with the same basic concepts. Early in 1957 a group of operations-research specialists from E. I. du Pont de Nemours got together with computer-applications experts at the Remington Rand division of Sperry Rand to design a procedure for scheduling chemical-plant construction. CPM was the result, and much of the credit for it belongs to James E. Kelley Jr., then with Remington Rand. Kelley not only exploited the critical-path concept but also introduced ways of "crashing" a project in an economical fashion. CPM caught on almost immediately in the construction industry.

CHART 1

HOW A COMPUTER DECIDES THE CHEAPEST SCHEDULE FOR A PROJECT

Job	Normal days	Normal cost	Crash days	Crash cost	Cost of crashing dollars per day
A	3	$140	2	$210	$70
B	6	215	5	275	60
C	2	160	1	240	80
D	4	130	3	180	50
E	2	170	1	250	80
F	7	165	4	285	40
G	4	210	3	290	80
H	3	110	2	160	50
Total		$1300		$1890	

Major industrial projects, such as the building of a ship or a factory or the development of a missile, involve so many activities that no human mind can keep close track of all that is going on, much less schedule every detail in the most efficient way. New mathematical techniques, however, are giving project managers a clearer view of their work and a better opportunity to use their judgment effectively. The essential steps in one of these new techniques, Critical Path Method, are demonstrated by the analysis of a tiny hypothetical project. The manager begins the scheduling by listing all the jobs that must be done (see chart above) together with estimates of normal time and cost for each. Next he estimates how much it would cost to rush each job to completion by a crash program. All this information is fed into a computer. As the totals show, the manager could get each job done as fast as possible by spending an extra $590. But he may be able to shorten the time of completing the whole project without "crashing" every job. This is what the computer will investigate.

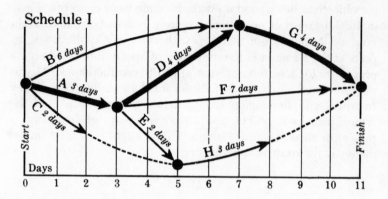

The manager diagrams the order in which the jobs must be done. This shows, for example, that C can be done in parallel with A but that D cannot be started until A is finished. The computer calculates the "critical path" (heavy black line) from this information. The jobs on this path determine the time (eleven days) needed to complete the whole project; the rest can be delayed somewhat (broken lines) without affecting the over-all schedule.

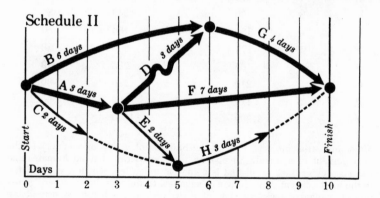

Next the computer calculates ways to shorten the over-all schedule by crashing some of the jobs. There may be several ways, but the computer selects the cheapest. The diagram above shows that if D is accelerated to three days instead of four, the over-all schedule can be reduced to ten days. Two more jobs, B and F, become part of a critical path, but there is still some leeway in C, E, and H. The cost of crashing D is an extra $50.

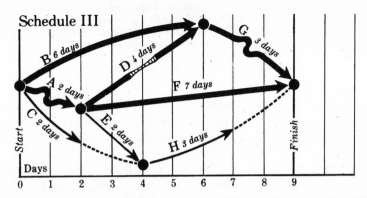

Again rescheduling the project so that it can be finished in nine days, the computer finds that it is best to crash both A and G by one day. Surprisingly, the extra effort put on these jobs makes it possible to relax a bit on D and allot the normal four days for its completion. Crashing A and G will cost a total of $150, but the relaxation of D saves $50, so the acceleration of the whole project from ten to nine days costs only $100 more.

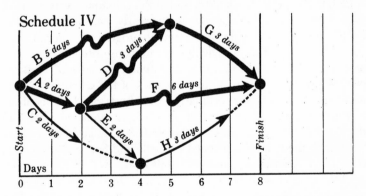

If the manager wants to lop another day from the schedule, he can do so most economically by crashing three jobs: B, D, and F. Although the chart shows that F could be shortened by as much as three days, the extra hurry would have no effect on the over-all schedule, so F is shortened by only one day. The manager has now spent $300 on the crash program, compared with the $590 he might have spent to crash all the jobs.

To decide which schedule is actually best from all viewpoints, the manager can instruct the computer to take other factors into account. There may be a penalty for failing to complete the project on schedule. Sometimes in actual practice contractors have found that they can make more profit by proceeding slowly and paying a penalty rather than paying heavy overtime. The chart below shows how the computer might include on its calculations indirect costs—e.g., overhead or penalties. In this example the indirect costs amount to a flat $110 per day, and the chart tells the manager that the cheapest schedule is the one that takes nine days.

Schedule	*I*	*II*	*III*	*IV*
Duration (days)	11	10	9	8
Direct cost	$1300	$1350	$1450	$1600
Indirect cost	$1210	$1100	$990	$880
Total cost	$2510	$2450	$2440	$2480

Other applications of CPM are now developing. Du Pont, Union Carbide, and several other manufacturing companies are using it to schedule maintenance on large plants. Most production lines have to be shut down and overhauled from time to time. By scheduling hundreds of maintenance steps in an optimal way CPM can often shorten the shutdown period and save thousands of dollars of production that would otherwise be lost.

PERT (Program Evaluation Review Technique) was born of sheer desperation. In 1956, during the early stages of the Navy's Polaris submarine-missile development program, a Special Projects Office was set up to manage this immense project. The men in charge found that all the conventional managerial methods were hopelessly inadequate to keep track of the schedule. Superimposed on the job of coordinating the efforts of 11,000 contractors was a degree of uncertainty as to when crucial research and development stages might be completed. So, Willard Fazar of the SPO, with the help of Lockheed's Missile and Space Division and consultants from Booz, Allen & Hamilton, devised PERT as a network flow chart with built-in uncertainty. Instead of assigning a single time estimate to each task, as Kelley had done with CPM, Fazar called for three estimates: optimistic, normal, and pessimistic. Such multiple estimating made the computations somewhat more difficult but they were still well within the capability of a high-speed computer.

PERT worked well from the time it was put into operation in 1958. Polaris chief Vice Admiral W. F. Raborn, Jr. has given the technique much credit for the fact that the development of the first Polaris missile required two years' less time than originally estimated. PERT is also beginning to find uses outside government projects. The most noteworthy to date was a schedule for the production of a Broadway play. PERT kept track of some 200 steps the producers had to take before the play opened—e.g., rent the theatre, sign the stars, hire a scenery designer, buy props, dispense publicity, and set a date for the dress rehearsal.

Both CPM and PERT are still in the evolutionary stage. Kelley has worked out a way to schedule a number of simultaneous projects that must share available resources, such as labor, machines, space, or money.

Most executive decisions hinge on the question of how to make the most of whatever is available—time, money, raw materials, manpower, production facilities, storage space, shipping. A manager may have to decide how many of each of three items he should produce. For example, the first item must be painstakingly assembled by hand; the second needs a great deal of machining; the third is bulky. If he were to concentrate on any one item, he would run short of labor, machines, or warehouse space. The decision technique called linear programing, a method older than and somewhat different from CPM or PERT, can tell him precisely the most profitable combination of the three items.

Some linear programs, such as those that portray the entire distribution system of a large company, involve several hundred interrelated variables. The programer starts by putting down in mathematical terms all the relations among the variables. Some are in the form of equations, others in the form of "inequalities"— e.g., mathematical statements that say a machine can produce *no more than* so many items per hour. By a mathematical stratagem the inequalities are then converted to equations. The variables outnumber the equations, so there is no unique algebraic solution. But such a system of equations can be made to yield optimum solutions—i.e., solutions that maximize profits, minimize costs, or make some other element in the business as small or large as possible. This is the purpose of linear programing.

The mathematical procedure generally used to find optimal solutions is the "simplex" method, invented in 1947 by George Dantzig. The method belies its name; it is extremely complicated. It is essentially a trial-and-error approach. But the groping for a solution is entirely methodical. It guarantees finding a better solution at each step and an optimal solution in a finite number of steps. Most practical linear-programming problems would take months, even years, to solve by hand, but a fast computer usually handles them in a few minutes.

Linear programing has been so thoroughly studied and so widely applied that experts usually classify problems into a number of standard types. They schedule truck and airline fleets with the transportation type. Another linear program, sometimes called the nutrition problem, decides how to mix animal feed so as to meet nutritional specifications at minimum cost; it is also used for blending gasoline to meet octane-number specifications. Paper and sheet-steel mills rely on the trim-loss reduction program to minimize waste when small orders are cut from large rolls.

Linear programing is especially valuable to the petroleum industry. There it is used more or less routinely for scheduling the distribution of products, balancing availability of raw crude with refinery operations so as to produce the most profitable assortment of products, blending gasoline, and even deciding where new refineries are needed.

In recent years linear programing has gained an important new dimension. In 1949, Albert W. Tucker, Harold W. Kuhn, and David Gale, following up a conjecture by the late John von Neumann, proved that every linear program has a shadow, called its "dual program." When a mathematician sets up a linear program to achieve one objective, he can in an easy step solve the dual program and thereby achieve a different objective. For example, the original program might find a production scheme that minimized costs for a fixed labor force and consumption of raw materials; the dual program would determine a system of internal pricing that would maximize the value of net output while balancing the direct costs of labor and raw materials. Looking at the solutions of both the original program and its dual gives the manager another degree of flexibility in making decisions. In addition to learning how to make the most profit with the machines at hand, he may be able to tell how to increase profits by installing more or different machines. Related mathematical techniques indicate what would happen if some of the variables were to change slightly. The same procedures also reveal how critical an error in the data might be; thus the manager knows when he can get away with an offhand estimate and when he has to make a careful study. The significance of all this additional information is that it enables the non-mathematical executive to ask questions he would naturally want to ask, even those that may not have occurred to him when the programing was begun. The decision theorist is able to use this kind of analysis also to increase the realism of his technique by blending hunches and judgments with the mathematics.

New mathematical inventions are beginning to break through some of the limitations of linear programing. Many programs are unwieldy; even the fastest computer takes several hours to perform the 200 million calculations needed to solve a program with 400 equations. Recently, however, Dantzig and Philip Wolfe worked out a computational shortcut, which they call the "decomposition" principle. It seems particularly applicable to situations that are not very tightly knit—e.g., the production scheduling of a company with many plants, each specializing in a few products that it feeds into a centralized marketing system. Decomposition is a mathematical way of chopping a huge program into many smaller ones and then solving each and coordinating the results in succession. As yet there have been no industrial applications, but several computer-service groups are coding the decomposition principle so that it can be fed into computers.

Another limitation of linear programing stems from the fact that it fails to distinguish between fractions and whole numbers. In some real problems only whole numbers are feasible. A program for scheduling a fleet of planes might, for example, tell an airline that 8.26 planes should be assigned to one particular route and 3.74 to another. The obvious step would be to round off the numbers to eight and four. But actually this is not safe; oddly enough, it might well prove more economical to assign six planes to each route. For such linear-programing problems Ralph E. Gomory, a young I.B.M. mathematician, has invented a brand-new technique called "integer programing." It usually requires a good deal more computation than the conventional simplex method, but it produces the best solution that can be expressed in whole numbers. Its greatest potential application appears to be in such problems as determining the overall costs of a new production plant where there is a major initial cost of building the plant as well as the continuing variable costs of its operation.

Elements of uncertainty complicate the decision process, often to such an extent that linear programing cannot produce a realistic solution in a reasonable time. In extreme cases a decision maker starts with almost total ignorance as to what decisions are possible, what the consequences might be, how long the situation will last, or even what goals he should seek. He gropes along, committing himself when he has to and changing his mind as his view becomes clearer. A new decision technique called "dynamic programing" formulates this groping in a logical way so that the decision maker behaves optimally at every stage—optimally, at least, within the limits of his knowledge at each stage.

The basic logic and the mathematics of dynamic programing are directly related to the theory of servomechanisms, the feedback controls that, for example, enable an autopilot to sense variations in an airplane's flight and bring it back on course. Richard Bellman, a Rand mathematician who is the leading exponent of dynamic programing, aims at a more sophisticated kind of control. Whereas an autopilot is designed for a specific goal—to keep the plane steady in flight—Bellman would like to design controls that would learn from experience what their goals should be and how best to attain them.

Bellman's theory is comprehensive enough to embrace decision making in business, economics, biology, and statistics, as well as engineering. The computational difficulties are formidable in many applications, but in the long run, dynamic programing promises to solve many hitherto intractable decision problems. It may, for example, help solve the dilemma of a physician who is testing a drug to determine whether it will cure a lethal disease. He is confronted with partly conflicting goals. As a scientist, he wants to prove conclusively whether the drug is effective, and he resolves to give it to only half his patients. But by following this plan he will almost surely doom the rest of the patients and so, as a practitioner, he is tempted to give the drug to all. Ordinarily, he must decide either to carry out a scientifically impeccable experiment or to do everything possible to cure patients. In principle, dynamic programing offers the physician a partial escape from this burdensome decision. He may be able to alter the testing procedure as he accumulates experimental results. If in the early stages of testing the drug seems to be effective, dynamic programing should tell him better than previous techniques how to administer it to a larger proportion of patients without casting doubts on the scientific validity of the test.

Dynamic programing is actually an extension of some concepts that have brought statistics into the realm of decision theory. During World War II a Columbia University statistician, Abraham Wald, devised a new way to decide how much statistical evidence was needed to support a conclusion.

Wald's "sequential" decision theory was based on earlier ideas that had been developed in the early thirties by Egon S. Pearson and Jerzy Neyman in England. Pearson and Neyman had included in their statistical methods the risks and consequences of drawing wrong conclusions. To these Wald had added another variable: the cost of sampling and testing. His methods had obvious practical appeal. Testing—indeed, acquiring knowledge of any sort—costs something, and the faster a statistician can make up his mind, the more money he saves.

As a consequence of Wald's theory, human judgment had to be embodied in statistical analysis. The statistician had to invent some formal procedure for deciding when to stop testing, and this procedure inevitably depended on expert opinion as to the consequences of drawing a wrong conclusion.

Some further attempts to extend the use of human judgment in statistics have aroused a major controversy. One group of statisticians advocates using expert opinion as if it were experimental evidence; this group is called the "neo-Bayesian" school after the Reverend Thomas Bayes, an eighteenth-century British contributor to the mathematics of probability theory. The neo-Bayesians use judgment to determine a priori probabilities—i.e., assumptions of likelihood—which can then be used mathematically to help calculate the probability that a given hypothesis is true. Neyman and most other conventional statisticians go along with this idea, but only up to a point. They employ a priori probabilities only when they are derived from repetitive observations of relevant data. In such cases there is a clear relationship between probability and frequency. They balk at the notion of applying a priori probabilities and judgment to analysis of once-in-a-lifetime situations.

These, significantly, are the situations that are involved in most major executive decisions—e.g., whether to merge with a company in another field, whether to bid on a missile contract, whether to open a plant in Europe. The neo-Bayesians would ask the executive for an opinion of his chances of success and they would use this "expert" opinion as if it were the result of an actual experiment.

The use of judgmental probability makes it possible to reinforce the subjective beliefs of a business executive—or a military commander—with a good deal of objectivity in the form of decision theory. Nevertheless, over-reliance on opinion can lead to bad decisions. Samuel S. Wilks cautions: "The danger is that you may be accepting a bad guess when you really should be buying more experimental knowledge."

Sir Solly Zuckerman, a British scientist who is one of the fathers of operations research, is greatly concerned because military analysts are applying probability laws that pertain to repetitive situations to once-in-a-lifetime situations. Writing in *Foreign Affairs*, Zuckerman warns: "If one decides wrongly about the use of nuclear weapons, we shall be in a situation which may never repeat itself. . . ."

Mathematical Programing

ALEXANDER HENDERSON AND ROBERT SCHLAIFER

Alexander Henderson was Professor of Economics at the Graduate School of Industrial Administration at Carnegie Institute of Technology. Robert Schlaifer is Professor of Business Administration at Harvard University. This paper comes from the Harvard Business Review *of May 1954.*

In recent years mathematicians have worked out a number of new procedures which make it possible for management to solve a wide variety of important company problems much faster, more easily, and more accurately than ever before. These procedures have sometimes been called "linear programing." Actually, linear programing describes only one group of them; "mathematical programing" is a more suitable title.

Mathematical programing is not just an improved way of getting certain jobs done. It is in every sense a new way. It is new in the sense that double-entry bookkeeping was new in the Middle Ages, or that mechanization in the office was new earlier in this century, or that automation in the plant is new today. Because mathematical programing is still new, the gap between the scientist and the businessman—between the researcher and the user—has not yet been bridged. Mathematical programing has made the news, but few businessmen really understand how it can be of use in their own companies.

Where to Ship · Let us look at a case where the technique was put to use as a routine operating procedure in an actual company.

The H. J. Heinz Company manufactures ketchup in half a dozen plants scattered across the United States from New Jersey to California and distributes this ketchup from about seventy warehouses located in all parts of the country.

In 1953 the company was in the fortunate position of being able to sell all it could produce, and supplies were allocated to warehouses in a total amount exactly equal to the total capacity of the plants. Management wished to supply these requirements at the lowest possible cost of freight; speed of shipment was not important. However, capacity in the West exceeded requirements in that part of the country, while the reverse was true in the East; for this reason a considerable tonnage had to be shipped from western plants to the East. In other words, the cost of freight could not be minimized by simply supplying each warehouse from the nearest plant.

This problem can immediately be recognized as a problem of programing because its essence is the minimization of cost subject to a fixed set of plant capacities and warehouse requirements. It can be handled by linear programing because the freight bill for shipments between any two points will be proportional to the quantity shipped. (The quantities involved are large enough so that virtually everything will move at carload rates under any shipping program which might be chosen.)

This is, in fact, the simplest possible kind of problem that can be solved by this method. Certain complexities which make solution by trial and error considerably more difficult than usual—in particular, the existence of water-competitive rates, which make it practical to send California ketchup all the way to the East Coast—add no real difficulty to the solution by linear programing. Given the list of plant capacities and warehouse requirements, plus a table of freight rates from every plant to every warehouse, one man with no equipment other than pencil and paper solved this problem for the first time in about twelve hours. After H. J. Heinz had adopted the method for regular use and clerks had been trained to become thoroughly familiar with the routine for this particular problem, the time required to develop a shipping program was considerably reduced.

The actual data of this problem have not been released by the company, but a fair representation of its magnitude is given by the similar but hypothetical examples of Exhibits 1 and 2, which show the data and solution of a problem of supplying twenty warehouses from twelve plants.

Exhibit 1 shows the basic data: the body of the table gives the freight rates, while the daily capacities of the plants and daily requirements of the warehouses are in the margins. For example, factory III, with a capacity of 3,000 cwt. per day, can supply warehouse G, with requirements of 940 cwt. per day, at a freight cost of seven cents per cwt.

Any reader who wishes to try his hand will quickly find that without a systematic procedure a great deal of work would be required to find a shipping program which would come reasonably close to satisfying these requirements and capacities at the lowest possible cost. But with the use of linear programing the problem is even easier than the Heinz problem.

Exhibit 2 gives the lowest-cost distribution program. For example, warehouse K is to get 700 cwt per day from factory I and 3,000 cwt. per day from factory III. On the other hand, factory III ships nothing to warehouse A, although Exhibit 1 shows that factory III could ship at less expense to this warehouse than to any other.

One of the most important advantages gained by the H. J. Heinz Company from the introduction of linear programing was relief of the senior members of the distribution department from the burden of preparing shipping programs. Previously the quarterly preparation of the program took a substantial amount of their time; now they pay only as much attention to this problem as they believe necessary to keep the feel of the situation, while the detailed development of the program has been handed over to clerks. Freed from the burden of working out what is after all only glorified arithmetic, they have this much more time to devote to matters which really require their experience and judgment.

An equally important gain, in the opinion of these officials themselves, is the peace of mind which results from being sure that the program is the lowest-cost program possible.

The direct dollars-and-cents saving in the company's freight bill was large enough by itself to make the use of this technique very

EXHIBIT 1

Table of Rates, Requirements, and Capacities

Factory	I	II	III	IV	V	VI	VII	VIII	IX	X	XI	XII	Daily requirements (cwt.)
						Freight rates (cents per cwt.)							
Warehouse A	16	16	6	13	24	13	6	31	37	34	37	40	1,820
B	20	18	8	10	22	11	8	29	33	25	35	38	1,530
C	30	23	8	9	14	7	9	22	29	20	38	35	2,360
D	10	15	10	8	10	15	13	19	19	15	28	34	100
E	31	23	16	13	10	16	20	14	17	17	25	28	280
F	24	14	19	13	13	14	18	9	14	13	29	25	730
G	27	23	7	11	23	8	16	6	10	11	16	28	940
H	34	25	15	4	27	15	16	9	16	17	13	16	1,130
J	38	29	17	11	16	27	17	19	8	18	19	11	4,150
K	42	43	21	22	16	10	21	18	24	16	17	15	3,700
L	44	49	25	23	18	6	13	19	15	12	10	13	2,560
M	49	40	29	21	10	15	14	21	12	29	14	20	1,710
N	56	58	36	37	6	25	8	19	9	21	15	26	580
P	59	57	44	33	5	21	6	10	8	33	15	18	30
Q	68	54	40	38	8	24	7	19	10	20	23	23	2,840
R	66	71	47	43	16	33	12	26	19	13	25	31	1,510
S	72	58	50	51	20	42	22	16	15	7	20	25	970
T	74	54	57	55	26	53	26	19	14	8	15	6	5,110
U	71	75	57	60	30	44	30	30	41	8	23	37	3,540
Y	73	72	63	56	37	49	40	31	31	10	8	25	4,410
Daily capacity (cwt.)	10,000	9,000	3,000	2,700	500	1,200	700	300	500	1,200	2,000	8,900	40,000

EXHIBIT 2

Lowest-cost Distribution Program

(DAILY SHIPMENTS FROM FACTORY TO WAREHOUSE IN CWT.)

Factory / Warehouse	I	II	III	IV	V	VI	VII	VIII	IX	X	XI	XII	Total	Row value
A	1,820												1,820	16
B	1,530												1,530	20
C		2,360											2,360	28
D	100												100	10
E		280											280	28
F		730											730	19
G	940												940	27
H				1,130									1,130	28
J		4,150											4,150	34
K	700		3,000										3,700	42
L	1,360					1,200							2,560	44
M		140		1,570									1,710	45
N	580												580	56
P								30					30	51
Q	810	1,340										500	2,650	59
R					500		700		500				1,700	66
S								90				880	970	57
T												5,110	5,110	42
U	2,160							180		1,200			3,540	71
Y											2,000	2,410	4,410	61
Total	10,000	9,000	3,000	2,700	500	1,200	700	300	500	1,200	2,000	8,900	40,000	
Column value	0	−5	−21	−24	−51	−38	−54	−41	−49	−63	−53	−36		

much worth while. The first shipping program produced by linear programing gave a projected semiannual freight cost several thousand dollars less than did a program prepared by the company's previous methods, and this comparison is far from giving a full measure of the actual freight savings to be anticipated.

Shipping schedules rest on estimates which are continuously subject to revision. The capacity figures in part represent actual stocks on hand at the plants, but in part they are based on estimates of future tomato crops; and the figures for requirements depend almost wholly on estimates of future sales. The fact that schedules are now quickly and accurately prepared by clerks has enabled the company to reschedule monthly rather than quarterly, thus making much better use of new information on crops and sales as it becomes available.

Furthermore, the risk of backhauling is very much reduced under the new system. It had always been company practice early in the season to hold "reserves" in regions of surplus production, in order to avoid the danger of shipping so much out of these regions that it became necessary to ship back into them when production and sales estimates were revised. In fact, these reserves were largely accidental leftovers: when it became really difficult to assign the last part of a factory's production, this remainder was called the reserve. Now the company can look at past history and decide in advance what reserve should be held at each factory and can set up its program to suit this estimate exactly. Since the schedule is revised each month, these reserves can be altered in the light of current information until they are finally reduced to nothing just before the new pack starts at the factory in question.

Many important problems of this same character unquestionably are prevalent in business. One such case, for instance, would be that of a newsprint producer who supplies about 220 customers all over the United States from six factories scattered over the width of Canada.

Similar problems arise where the cost of transportation is measured in time rather than in money. In fact, the first efforts to solve problems of this sort systematically were made during World War II in order to minimize the time spent by ships in ballast. Specified cargo had to be moved from specified origins to specified destinations; there was usually no return cargo, and the problem was to decide to which port the ship should be sent in ballast to pick up its next cargo. An obviously similar problem is the routing of empty freight cars, and a trucker operating on a nationwide scale might face the same problem with empty trucks.

Where to Produce · When ketchup shipments were programed for the H. J. Heinz Company, factory capacities and warehouse requirements were fixed before the shipping program was worked out, and the only cost which could be reduced by programing was the cost of freight. Since management had decided in advance how much to produce at each plant, all production costs were "fixed" so far as the programing problem was concerned.

The same company faces a different problem in connection with another product, which is also produced in a number of plants and shipped to a number of warehouses. In this case, the capacity of the plants exceeds the requirements of the warehouses. The cost of production varies from one plant to another, and the problem is thus one of satisfying the requirements at the least *total* cost. It is as important to reduce the cost of production (by producing in the right place) as it is to reduce the cost of freight (by supplying from the right place). In other words, management must now decide two questions instead of one: (*a*) How much is each factory to produce? (*b*) Which warehouses should be supplied by which factories?

It is tempting to try to solve these two problems one at a time and thus simplify the job, but in general it will not be possible to get the lowest total cost by first deciding where to produce and then deciding where to ship. It is obviously better to produce in a high-cost plant if the additional cost can be more than recovered through savings in freight.

This double problem can be handled by linear programing if we may assume (as businessmen usually do) that the cost of production at any one plant is the sum of a "fixed" cost independent of volume and a "variable" cost proportional to volume in total but fixed per unit, and if these costs are known. The variable cost is handled directly by the linear programing procedure, while the fixed part is handled by a method which will be explained later.

Actually, the problem can be much more complicated and still lend itself to solution by linear programing. For example, we can bring in the possibility of using overtime, or of buying raw materials at one price up to a certain quantity and at another price beyond that quantity.

Exhibit 3 shows the cost information needed to solve a hypothetical example of this sort. It is assumed that there are only four plants and four warehouses, but any number could be brought into the problem.

In our first approximation (which we shall modify later) we shall assume that no plant will be closed down entirely and, therefore, that "fixed costs" are really fixed and can be left out of the picture. Like Exhibit 1, Exhibit 3 shows the freight rates from each plant to each warehouse, the available daily capacity at each plant, and the daily requirements of each warehouse; it also shows the "variable" (fixed-per-unit) cost of normal production at each plant and the additional per-unit cost of overtime production. The total capacity is greater than the total requirements even if the factories work only normal time.

EXHIBIT 3
Cost Information for Double Problem
A. Warehouse requirements (tons per day)

Warehouse	A	B	C	D	Total
Requirements	90	140	75	100	405

B. Factory capacities (tons per day)

Factory	I	II	III	IV	Total
Normal capacity	70	130	180	110	490
Additional capacity on overtime	25	40	60	30	155

C. Variable costs (per ton)

Factory	I	II	III	IV
Normal production cost	$30	$36	$24	$30
Overtime premium	15	18	12	15
Freight rates to:				
Warehouse A	$14	$ 9	$21	$18
B	20	14	27	24
C	18	12	29	20
D	19	15	27	23

On the basis of these data, the lowest-cost solution is given by part A of Exhibit 4. It is scarcely surprising that this solution calls for no use of overtime. So long as fixed costs are taken as really fixed, it turns out that it is best to use the entire normal capacity of factories I, II, and III, and to use 25 tons of factory IV's normal capacity of 110 tons per day. The remaining 85 tons of normal capacity at IV are left unused. The total variable cost under this schedule (freight cost plus variable production cost) will be $19,720 per day.

Presented with this result, management would certainly ask whether it is sensible to keep all four factories open when one of

EXHIBIT 4

LOWEST-COST DISTRIBUTION PROGRAM
(DAILY SHIPMENTS IN TONS FROM FACTORY TO WAREHOUSE)

A. With all four factories open

Factory	I	II	III	IV	Total
Warehouse A			90		90
B		80	60		140
C		50		25	75
D	70		30		100
Idle normal capacity				85	85
Total	70	130	180	110	490

B. With factory I closed

Factory		II	III	IV	Total
Warehouse A			90		90
B		130	10		140
C				75	75
D			80	20	100
Idle normal capacity				15	15
Total		130	180	110	420

C. With factory IV closed

Factory	I	II	III		Total
Warehouse A			90		90
B		55	85		140
C		75			75
D	70		30		100
Total	70	130	205		405

them is being left about 80 per cent idle. Even without incurring overtime, factory I, the smallest plant, could be closed and the load redistributed among the other plants. If this is done, the lowest-cost distribution of the requirements among factories II, III, and IV is that given by part *B* of Exhibit 4. Under this program the total variable cost would be $19,950 per day, or $230 per day more than under the program of Exhibit 4*A*, which depended on the use of all four plants. If more than $230 per day of fixed costs can be saved by closing down factory I completely, it will pay to do so; otherwise it will not.

It might be still better, however, to close down some plant other than factory I even at the cost of a certain amount of overtime. In particular, a very little overtime production (25 tons per day) would make it possible to close factory IV. A person asked to look into this possibility might reason as follows: Under the shipping schedule of Exhibit 4*A*, the only use of factory IV's capacity is to supply 25 tons per day to warehouse *C*. Looking at Exhibit 3 for a replacement for this supply, he would get the following information on costs per ton:

Factory	Normal cost of production	Overtime premium	Freight to warehouse C	Total
I	$30	$15	$18	$63
II	36	18	12	66
III	24	12	29	65

Apparently the cheapest way of using overtime, if it is to be used at all, would be to produce the needed 25 tons per day at factory I and ship them to warehouse *C* at a total variable cost of $63 per ton. Under the program of Exhibit 4*A*, with all plants in use, warehouse *C* was supplied from factory IV at a total variable cost of $30 for production plus $20 for freight, or a total of $50 per ton. The change would thus seem to add a total of $325 per day (25 tons times $13 per ton which is the difference between $63 and $50 per ton).

But, in fact, closing factory IV need not add this much to the cost of the program. If we take factory IV out of the picture and then program to find the best possible distribution of the output of the remaining plants, we discover that the program of part *C* of Exhibit 4 satisfies all requirements at a total variable cost of $19,-

995 per day, or only $275 per day more than with all plants in use. The overtime is performed by factory III, which does not supply warehouse C at all.

This last result deserves the reader's attention. *Once a change was made in a single part of the program, the best adjustment was a general readjustment of the entire program.* But such a general readjustment is impractical unless complete programs can be developed quickly and at a reasonable cost. It is rarely clear in advance whether the work will prove profitable, and management does not want to throw a heavy burden of recalculation on senior personnel every time a minor change is made. Mathematical programing avoids these difficulties. Even minor changes in the data can be made freely despite the fact that complete recalculations of the program are required, because the work can be done quickly and accurately by clerks or machines.

We can proceed to compute the lowest possible cost of supplying the requirements with factory II or factory III closed down completely. We can then summarize the results for all alternatives like this:

Total freight plus variable production cost

All four factories in use	$19,720
Factory I closed, no overtime	19,950
Factory II closed, overtime at factory III	20,515
Factory III closed, overtime at factories I, II, and IV	21,445
Factory IV closed, overtime at factory III	19,995

Management now has the information on variable costs which it needs in order to choose rationally among three alternatives: (1) operating all four plants with a large amount of idle normal capacity; (2) shutting down factory I and still having a little idle normal capacity; (3) shutting down factory II, III, or IV and incurring overtime. Its choice will depend in part on the extent to which fixed costs can be eliminated when a particular plant is completely closed; it may depend even more on company policies regarding community relations or some other nonfinancial consideration. Mathematical programing cannot replace judgment, but it can supply some of the factual information which management needs in order to make judgments.

Problems of this general type are met in purchasing as well as in producing and selling. A company which buys a standard raw material at many different geographical locations and ships it to a number of scattered plants for processing will wish to minimize the total cost of purchase plus freight; here the solution can be obtained in exactly the same way as just discussed. The Department of Defense is reported to have made substantial savings by using linear programing to decide where to buy and where to send certain standard articles which it obtains from a large number of suppliers for direct shipment to military installations.

Linear Programming:
Examples and Concepts

George Dantzig

George Dantzig is head of the Operations Research Center at the University of California, Berkeley. This article comes from his book, Linear Programming and Extensions, *published in 1963.*

THE PROGRAMMING PROBLEM

Industrial production, the flow of resources in the economy, the exertion of military effort in a war theater—all are complexes of numerous interrelated activities. Differences may exist in the goals to be achieved, the particular processes involved, and the magnitude of effort. Nevertheless, it is possible to abstract the underlying essential similarities in the management of these seemingly disparate systems. To do this entails a look at the structure and state of the system, and at the objective to be fulfilled, in order to *construct a statement of the actions to be performed, their timing, and their quantity (called a "program" or "schedule"), which will permit the system to move from a given status toward the defined objective.*

If the system exhibits a structure which can be represented by a mathematical equivalent, called a mathematical model, and if the objective can also be so quantified, then some computational method may be evolved for choosing the best schedule of actions among alternatives. Such use of mathematical models is termed mathematical programming. The observation that a number of military, economic, and industrial problems can be expressed (or reasonably approximated) by mathematical systems of linear inequalities and equations[1] has helped give rise to the development of linear programming.

The following three examples are typical programming problems which can be formulated linearly; they are analogous to the ones which originated research in this area. It is well to have them in mind before we discuss the general characteristics of linear programming problems.

The objective of the system in each of the three examples to be considered happens to be the minimization of total costs measured in monetary units. In other applications, however, it could be to minimize direct labor costs or to maximize the number of assembled parts or to maximize the number of trained students with a specified percentage distribution of skills, etc.

1. *A cannery example.* Suppose that the three canneries of a distributor are located in Portland (Maine), Seattle, and San Diego. The canneries can fill 250, 500, and 750 cases of tins per day, respectively. The distributor operates five warehouses around the country, in New York, Chicago, Kansas City, Dallas, and San Francisco. Each of the warehouses can sell 300 cases per day. The distributor wishes to determine the number of cases to be shipped from the three canneries to the five warehouses so that each warehouse should obtain as many cases as it can sell daily at the minimum total transportation cost.

The problem is characterized by the fifteen possible *activities* of shipping cases from each of the canneries to each of the warehouses (Fig. 1). There are fifteen *unknown activity levels* (to be determined) which are the *amounts* to be shipped along the fifteen routes. This *shipping schedule* is generally referred to as the *program*. There are a number of constraints that a shipping schedule must satisfy to be feasible: namely, the schedule must

1. The reader should especially note we have used the word *inequalities*. Systems of linear inequalities are quite general; linear inequality relations such as $x \geqq 0$, $x + y \leqq 7$ can be used to express a variety of common restrictions, such as quantities purchased, x, must not be negative or the total amount of purchases, $x + y$, must not exceed 7, etc.

FIGURE 1

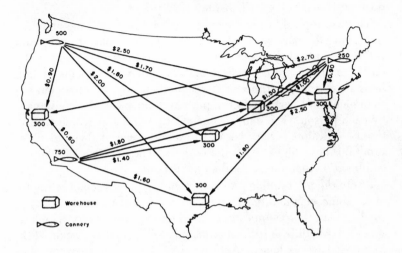

The problem: find a least cost plan of shipping from canneries to warehouses (the costs per case, availabilities and requirements are as indicated).

show that each warehouse will receive the required number of cases and that no cannery will ship more cases than it can produce daily. (Note there is one constraint for each warehouse and one for each cannery.) Several *feasible shipping schedules* may exist which would satisfy these constraints, but some will involve larger shipping costs than others. The problem then is to determine an *optimal shipping schedule*—one that has least costs.

2. *The housewife's problem.* A family of five lives on the modest salary of the head of the household. A constant problem is to determine the weekly menu after due consideration of the needs and tastes of the family and the prices of foods. The husband must have 3,000 calories per day, the wife is on a 1,500-calorie reducing diet, and the children require 3,000, 2,700, and 2,500 calories per day, respectively. According to the prescription of the family doctor, these calories must be obtained for each member by eating not more than a certain amount of fats and carbohydrates and not less than a certain amount of proteins. The diet, in fact, places emphasis on proteins. In addition, each member of

the household must satisfy his or her daily vitamin needs. The problem is to assemble menus, one for each week, that will minimize costs according to Thursday food prices.

This is a typical linear programming problem: the possible activities are the purchasing of foods of different types; the program is the amounts of different foods to be purchased; the constraints on the problem are the calorie and vitamin requirements of the household, and the upper or lower limits set by the physician on the amounts of carbohydrates, proteins, and fats to be consumed by each person. The number of food combinations which satisfy these constraints is very large. However, some of these feasible programs have higher costs than others. The problem is to find a combination that minimizes the total expense.

3. *On-the-job training.* A manufacturing plant is contracting to make some commodity. Its present work force is considerably smaller than the one needed to produce the commodity within a specified schedule of different amounts to be delivered each week for several weeks hence. Additional workers must, therefore, be hired, trained, and put to work. The present force can either work and produce at some rate of output, or it can train some fixed number of new workers, or it can do both at the same time according to some fixed rate of exchange between output and the number of new workers trained. Even were the crew to spend one entire week training new workers, it would be unable to train the required number. The next week, the old crew *and* the newly trained workers may either work or train new workers, or may both work and train, and so on. The commodity is semi-perishable so that amounts produced before they are needed will have to be stored at a specified cost. The problem is to determine the hiring, production, and storage program that will minimize total costs.

This, too, is a linear programming problem, although with the special property, not shared with the previous two examples, of *scheduling activities through time.* The activities in this problem are the assignment of old workers to either of two jobs, production or training, and the hiring of new workers each week. The quantities of these activities are restricted by the number of workers available at the beginning of each week and by the instructor-student ratio. The cumulative output produced by all workers through the number of weeks in the contractual period has to equal or exceed the required output. A possible production-training program is shown in Fig. 2. The problem can now be stated

FIGURE 2

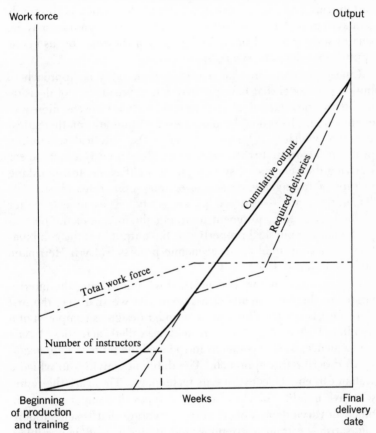

The problem: determine a least-cost hiring, production and storage program to meet required deliveries.

more precisely: determine the proper balance between hiring and training of workers, between teaching and production, and between over- and under-production in order to minimize total costs.

LINEAR PROGRAMMING DEFINED

We shall use the term *model building* to express the process of putting together of symbols representing objects according to certain rules, to form a structure, *the model*, which corresponds to a system under study in the real world. The symbols may be small-scale replicas of bricks and girders or they may be, as in our application, algebraic symbols.

Linear programming has a certain philosophy or approach to building a model that has application to a broad class of decision problems encountered in government, industry, economics, and engineering. It probably possesses the simplest mathematical structure which can be used to solve the practical scheduling problems associated with these areas. Because it is a method for studying the behavior of systems, it exemplifies the distinguishing feature of management science, or operations research, to wit: "Operations are considered as an entity. The subject matter studied is not the equipment used, nor the morale of the participants, nor the physical properties of the output, it is the combination of these in total as an economic process." (Cyril Herrmann and John Magee, 1953).

Linear programming[2] is concerned with describing the interrelations of the components of a system. As we shall see, the first step consists in regarding a system under design as composed of a number of elementary functions that are called "activities."[3] As a consequence, T. C. Koopmans introduced the term *activity analysis* to describe this approach. The different activities in which a system can engage constitute its technology. These are the representative building blocks of different types that might be recombined in varying amounts to rear a structure that is self-supporting, satisfies certain restrictions, and attains as well as possible a stated objective. Representing this structure in mathematical terms often results in a system of linear inequalities and equations; when this is so, it is called a linear programming model. Like

2. The term "linear programming" was suggested to the author by T. C. Koopmans in 1951 as an alternative to the earlier form, "programming in a linear structure."

3. The term "activity" in this connection is military in origin. It has been adopted in preference to the term "process," used by von Neumann in "A Model of General Economic Equilibrium."

architects, people who use linear programming models manipulate "on paper" the symbolic representations of the building blocks (activities) until a satisfactory design is obtained. The theory of linear programming is concerned with scientific procedures for arriving at the best design, given the technology, the required specifications, and the stated objective.

To be a linear programming model, the system must satisfy certain assumptions of proportionality, nonnegativity, and additivity. How this comes about will be discussed below. It is important to realize in trying to construct models of real-life situations, that life seldom, if ever, presents a clearly defined linear programming problem, and that simplification and neglect of certain characteristics of reality are as necessary in the application of linear programming as they are in the use of any scientific tool in problem solving.

The rule is to *neglect the negligible.* In the cannery example, for instance, the number of cases shipped and the number received may well differ because of accidental shipping losses. This difference is not known in advance and may be unimportant. In the optimum diet example the true nutritional value of each type of food differs from unit to unit, from season to season, from one source of food to another. Likewise, production rates and teaching quality will vary from one worker to another and from one hour to another. In some applications it may be necessary to give considerable thought to the differences between reality and its representation as a mathematical model to be sure that the differences are reasonably small and to assure ourselves that the computational results will be operationally useful.

What constitutes the proper simplification, however, is subject to individual judgment and experience. People often disagree on the adequacy of a certain model to describe the situation.

BASIC CONCEPTS

Suppose that the system under study (which may be one actually in existence, or one which we wish to design) is a complex of machines, people, facilities, and supplies. It has certain over-all reasons for its existence. For the military it may be to provide a striking force, or for industry it may be to produce certain types of products.

The linear programming approach is to consider a system as decomposable into a number of elementary functions, the *activities*. An activity is thought of as a kind of "black box"[4] into which flow tangible inputs, such as men, material, and equipment, and out of which may flow the products of manufacture, or the trained crews of the military. What happens to the inputs inside the "box" is the concern of the engineer or of the educator; to the programmer, only the rates of flow into and out of the activity are of interest. The various kinds of flow are called *items*.

The quantity of each activity is called the *activity level*. To change the activity level it is necessary to change the flows into and out of the activity.

Assumption 1: Proportionality · In the linear programming model the quantities of flow of various items into and out of the activity are always proportional to the activity level. If we wish to double the activity level, we simply double all the corresponding flows for the unit activity level. For instance, in Example 3, if we wish to double the number of workers trained in a period, we would have to double the number of instructors for that period and the number of workers hired. This characteristic of the linear programming model is known as the proportionality assumption.

Assumption 2: Nonnegativity · While any positive multiple of an activity is possible, negative quantities of activities are not possible. For instance, in Example 1, a negative number of cases cannot be shipped. Another example occurs in a well-known classic: the Mad Hatter, you may recall, in *Alice's Adventures in Wonderland*, was urging Alice to have some more tea, and Alice was objecting that she couldn't see how she could take more when she hadn't had any. "You mean, you don't see how you can take *less* tea," said the Hatter, "it is very easy to take more than nothing." Lewis Carroll's point was probably lost on his pre-linear-programming audience, for why should one emphasize the obvious fact that the activity of "taking tea" cannot be done in negative quantity? Perhaps it was Carroll's way of saying that mathemati-

4. Black box: Any system whose detailed internal nature one willfully ignores.

cians had been so busy for centuries extending the number system from integers, to fractions, to negative, to imaginary numbers, that they had given little thought on how to keep the variables of their problems in their original nonnegative range. This characteristic of the variables of the linear programming model is known as the nonnegativity assumption.

Assumption 3: Additivity · The next step in building a model is to specify that the system of activities be complete in the sense that a complete accounting by activity can be made of each item. To be precise, for each item it is required that the total amount specified by the system as a whole equals the sum of the amounts flowing into the various activities minus the sum of the amounts flowing out. Thus, each item, in our abstract system, is characterized by a *material balance equation*, the various terms of which represent the flows into or out of the various activities. In the cannery example, the number of cases sent into a warehouse must be completely accounted for by the amounts flowing out of the shipping activities from various canneries including possible storage or disposal of any excess. This characteristic of the linear programming model is known as the additivity assumption.

Assumption 4: Linear Objective Function · One of the items in our system is regarded as "precious" in the sense that the total quantity of it produced by the system measures the payoff. The precious item could be skilled labor, completed assemblies, an input resource that is in scarce supply like a limited monetary budget. The contribution of each activity to the total payoff is the amount of the precious item that flows into or out of each activity. Thus, if the objective is to maximize profits, activities that require money contribute negatively and those that produce money contribute positively to total profits. The housewife's expenditures for each type of food, in Example 2, is a negative contribution to total "profits" of the household; there are no activities in this example that contribute positively. This characteristic of the linear programming model is known as the linear objective assumption.

The Standard Linear Programming Problem · The determination of values for the *levels* of activities, which are positive or zero, such that flows of each item (for these activity levels) satisfy the material balance equations and such that the value of the payoff is a maximum is called the standard linear programming problem. The representation of a real system, as in any one of the three examples above, as a mathematical system which exhibits the above characteristics, is called a linear programming model. The problem of programming the activities of the real system is thus transformed into the problem of finding the solution of the linear programming model.

Linear Programming:
A Graphical Illustration

ROBERT DORFMAN

Robert Dorfman is Professor of Economics at Harvard University. This selection is from his article "Mathematical or Linear Programming," which appeared in the 1953 American Economic Review.

Let us consider an hypothetical automobile company equipped for the production of both automobiles and trucks. This company, then, can perform two economic tasks, and we assume that it has a single process for accomplishing each. These two tasks, the manufacture of automobiles and that of trucks, compete for the use of the firm's facilities. Let us assume that the company's plant is organized into four departments: (1) sheet metal stamping, (2) engine assembly, (3) automobile final assembly, and (4) truck final assembly—raw materials, labor, and all other components being available in virtually unlimited amounts at constant prices in the open market.

The capacity of each department of the plant is, of course, limited. We assume that the metal stamping department can turn out sufficient stampings for 25,000 automobiles or 35,000 trucks per month. We can then calculate the combinations of automobile and truck stampings which this department can produce. Since the department can accommodate 25,000 automobiles per month, each automobile requires 1/25,000 or 0.004 per cent of monthly capacity. Similarly each truck requires 0.00286 per cent of monthly capacity. If, for example, 15,000 automobiles were manufactured they would require 60 per cent of metal stamping capacity and the remaining 40 per cent would be sufficient to produce stampings for 14,000 trucks. Then 15,000 automobiles and 14,000 trucks could be produced by this department at full operation. This is, of course, not the only combination of automobiles and trucks which could be produced by the stamping department at full operation. In Figure 1, the line labeled "Metal Stamping" represents all such combinations.

Similarly we assume that the engine assembly department has monthly capacity for 33,333 automobile engines or 16,667 truck engines or, again, some combination of fewer automobile and truck engines. The combinations which would absorb the full capacity of the engine assembly department are shown by the "Engine Assembly" line in Figure 1. We assume also that the automobile assembly department can accommodate 22,500 automobiles per month and the truck assembly department 15,000 trucks. These limitations are also represented in Figure 1.

We regard this set of assumptions as defining two processes: the production of automobiles and the production of trucks. The process of producing an automobile yields, as an output, one automobile and absorbs, as inputs, 0.004 per cent of metal stamping capacity, 0.003 per cent of engine assembly capacity, and 0.00444 per cent of automobile assembly capacity. Similarly the process of producing a truck yields, as an output, one truck and absorbs, as inputs, 0.00286 per cent of metal stamping capacity, 0.006 per cent of engine assembly capacity, and 0.00667 per cent of truck assembly capacity.

The economic choice facing this firm is the selection of the numbers of automobiles and trucks to be produced each month, subject to the restriction that no more than 100 per cent of the capacity of any department can be used. Or, in more technical phraseology, the choice consists in deciding at what level to employ each of the two available processes. Clearly, if automobiles alone are produced, at most 22,500 units per month can be made, automobile assembly being the effective limitation. If only trucks are produced, a maximum of 15,000 units per month can be made

FIGURE 1

CHOICES OPEN TO AN AUTOMOBILE FIRM

because of the limitation on truck assembly. Which of these alternatives should be adopted, or whether some combination of trucks and automobiles should be produced depends on the relative profitability of manufacturing trucks and automobiles. Let us assume, to be concrete, that the sales value of an automobile is $300 greater than the total cost of purchased materials, labor, and other direct costs attributable to its manufacture. And, similarly, that the sale value of a truck is $250 more than the direct cost of manufacturing it. Then the net revenue of the plant for any month is 300 times the number of automobiles produced plus 250 times the number of trucks. For example, 15,000 automobiles and 6,000 trucks would yield a net revenue of $6,000,000. There are many combinations of automobiles and trucks which would yield this same net revenue; 10,000 automobiles and 12,000 trucks is another one. In terms of Figure 1, all combinations with a net revenue of $6,000,000 lie on a straight line, to be specific, the line labelled $6,000,000 in the figure.

A line analogous to the one which we have just described corresponds to each possible net revenue. All these lines are parallel, since their slope depends only on the relative profitability of the two activities. The greater the net revenue, of course, the higher the line. A few of the net revenue lines are shown in the figure by the dashed parallel lines.

Each conceivable number of automobiles and trucks produced corresponds to a point on the diagram, and through each point there passes one member of the family of net revenue lines. Net revenue is maximized when the point corresponding to the number of automobiles and trucks produced lies on the highest possible net revenue line. Now the effect of the capacity restrictions is to limit the range of choice to outputs which correspond to points lying inside the area bounded by the axes and by the broken line ABCDE. Since net revenue increases as points move out from the origin, only points which lie on the broken line need be considered. Beginning then with Point A and moving along the broken line we see that the boundary of the accessible region intersects higher and higher net revenue lines until point C is reached. From there on, the boundary slides down the scale of net revenue lines. Point C therefore corresponds to the highest attainable net revenue. At point C the output is 20,370 automobiles and 6,481 trucks, yielding a net revenue of $7,731,481 per month.

The "Game" of Business

John McDonald

John MacDonald is an editor of Fortune
*Magazine. This article is taken from his
book,* Strategy in Poker, Business, and War,
first published in 1950.

The core of business is the market. The core of the market is the relationship of buyer and seller, whether either is an individual or a corporation. The theory of games investigates the interior of this relationship with game models.

From the standpoint of the individual there are three possible economic situations on earth: one man alone, two men, or three or more men. One man is Robinson Crusoe alone on an island. He plays there the game of solitaire, maximizing his gain uncomplicated by anything but the forces of nature, which are predictable, at least in such terms as probable rainfall and the probability of a tornado.

If there are two men on earth, the individual enters into the relation of exchange (buyer-seller), in which the problem of the other fellow appears; he can no longer maximize his gain but must seek a limitation of the possibilities in an optimum. But if there are three men, the novelty occurs that two of them may gain more by combining against the third (e.g., two sellers against a buyer, or vice versa). These three situations are the same as those found in games.

Any industry serves as an example of strategical game play. Take the liquor industry, which like steel, oil or automobiles has only a few sellers. The following story was told at length in *Fortune* magazine. Samuel Bronfman of Seagram had come down from Canada at the time of repeal and built his organization on blended whiskey in the tradition of Canadian and Scotch whiskeys. U.S. distillers, slow to adopt blends, preferred to sell the traditional American rye and bourbon. But blended whiskey could be nationally advertised to better advantage (rye and bourbon being largely regional); and Bronfman made the most of it. His marketing strategy consisted of blends, brand names and mild taste. Eventually there was a contest for leadership in the industry between Seagram and Schenley. Lewis Rosenstiel of Schenley, an old-school U.S. distiller, divided his attention between blends and straights. Now whiskey is made at one time to be sold four or more years later, and there is a corresponding risk in the inventory. Keep too little and you may run short. Keep too much and you may get stuck (whiskey consumption roughly follows the income curve; and as in any industry total inventories can get out of hand, resulting, in the absence of mandatory fair trade laws, in occasional price wars). "Holidays" during World War II had eliminated several crops of whiskey and inventories generally were low. Rosenstiel is known as an inventory strategist. He came out of the war period with brand sales off but with perhaps half of the remaining aged whiskey inventory in the U.S. Bronfman of Seagram had used up a large part of his whiskey inventory in gaining record brand sales. In this situation, they had a contest for the leadership, a kind of two-man game within the industry.

Facing a forthcoming shortage, Bronfman could either buy scarce bulk whiskey at a losing price and maintain Seagram's brand sales with a decline in profits, or maintain his rate of profit out of his remaining inventory with a decline in brand sales—or follow a mixed policy. In any event he could not maximize both brand sales and profits. Rosenstiel could sell the inventory to Bronfman at high bulk prices and no sales cost and thus maximize profits in the immediate circumstance; or he could put the inventory into Schenley brands with an expensive and risky sales campaign to raise brand sales at less profit. Like Bronfman, but for different reasons, he could not maximize both brand sales and profits.

Nor could the policies of the antagonists fail to conflict; for Rosenstiel, who, having the better inventory, had the dominant choice, could reconcile their difference only by taking profit and giving Bronfman the market (brand sales), i.e., take short-term gains at the cost of long-term losses. Within limits, Bronfman would have been glad to buy the market (take short-term losses with long-term gains)—if Rosenstiel would let him. But Rosenstiel wouldn't. Each sought an optimum move on a strategical basis. The game broadened out with larger numbers as Bronfman got some whiskey from another source. Rosenstiel opened a "back-label" campaign to make his aged stocks pay off. The consequences of the struggle have not been told, but whatever they are, they are the consequences of conscious strategy. Theoretically, Seagram and Schenley had another alternative, namely, to combine. There are good reasons why they would not, yet each of these corporate individuals like so many others in industry had grown large through combination.

The three-man coalition game can be played as an auction with one seller and two buyers. The seller has a reserve price of, say, $10 on the object to be sold. The first buyer is willing to go to not more than $15; the second buyer to not more than $20. Clearly the second buyer being the stronger will get the object. Ordinarily he is expected to get it for something over $15. But suppose the second buyer approaches the first and makes a deal to eliminate competitive bidding. He can then get the object for something over $10. The deal, however, requires a division of the spoils. The second, stronger buyer must pay the first, weaker buyer something for making the coalition. That payment must be enough to yield the second buyer the "best" profit, and yet enough to ensure that his partner will remain in the coalition: two maximums which must be resolved. For another, rival deal is possible —in game theory but not in classical economics—namely this: The seller may cross the market and break up the coalition by paying something to the second buyer to restore the bidding and thereby push the selling price back above $15. Thus each two-man game in this three-man game is under the influence of the other possible two-man games, in arriving at the distribution payment.

In the theory of games a number of solutions, i.e., distribution schemes, are possible, some of which are enforceable and therefore dominate others. In classical theory the weaker buyer gets nothing; in game theory he gets a bribe, and the bribe will be expressed in the price. Here the difference between classical economics and game theory can be shown with simple numbers. In classical theory the price is between $15 and $20 (all going to the seller). In game theory it is between $10 and $20, depending on the bargaining ability of the players.

The basic strategy of organizers of industry from the beginning has been to substitute combination for large-number competition. The value which J. P. Morgan put on combination was indicated in the capitalization of the United States Steel Corporation in 1901. The Corporation, which brought together about 65 percent of the steel capacity of the United States, was capitalized at about twice the tangible value given to its separate properties before combination. The specific combinative value (about three-quarters of a billion dollars minus an unknown value put on "good will") was expressed in the new common stock—attacked as "watered stock"—which eventually paid off as the technical and strategical market advantages of combination were realized. The Corporation later met rivalry from other combinations which were organized in opposition to it.

Rockefeller's genius similarly expressed itself in combinations. But some of these early combinations, as they were organized, were unwieldy. Standard Oil stockholders probably benefited from the trust's court-ordered dissolution in 1911. It became impolitic thereafter, under the Sherman Act, for one organization to hold an overwhelming share of the market. For that reason or because its ability to compete against counter-combinations was injured by organizational and management defects, the Steel Corporation retreated to its present holdings of about one-third of the industry's ingot capacity. Its present leadership of the industry is maintained by modern market techniques described in oligopoly and game theory.

Introduction to Game Theory

J. D. WILLIAMS

J. D. Williams is head of the mathematics department at the RAND Corporation. This article comes from his book, The Compleat Strategyst, *published in 1954.*

The number of persons involved is one of the important criteria for classifying and studying games, 'person' meaning a distinct set of interests. Another criterion has to do with the payoff: What happens at the end of the game? Say at the end of the hand in poker? Well, in poker there is usually just an exchange of assets. If there are two persons, say you (Blue) and we (Red), then if you should win $10, we would lose $10. In other words,

$$\text{Blue winnings} = \text{Red losses}$$

or, stated otherwise,

$$\text{Blue winnings} - \text{Red losses} = 0$$

We may also write it as

$$\text{Blue payoff} + \text{Red payoff} = \$10 - \$10 = 0$$

by adopting the convention that winnings are positive numbers and that losses are negative numbers.

It needn't have turned out just that way; i.e., that the sum of the payoffs is zero. For instance, if the person who wins the pot has to contribute 10 percent toward the drinks and other incidentals, as to the cop on the corner, then the sum of the pay-offs is not zero; in fact

$$\text{Blue payoff} + \text{Red payoff} = \$9 - \$10 = -\$1$$

The above two cases illustrate a fundamental distinction among games: It is important to know whether or not the sum of the payoffs, counting winnings as positive and losses as negative, to all players is zero. If it is, the game is known as a *zero-sum game*. If it is not, the game is known (mathematicians are not very imaginative at times) as a *non-zero-sum game*. The importance of the distinction is easy to see: In the zero-sum case, we are dealing with a good, clean, closed system; the two players and the valuables are locked in the room. It will require a certain effort to specify and to analyze such a game. On the other hand, the non-zero-sum game contains all the difficulties of the zero-sum game, plus additional troubles due to the need to incorporate new factors. This can be appreciated by noting that we can restore the situation by adding a fictitious player—Nature, say, or the cop. Then we have

$$\text{Blue payoff} = \$9$$
$$\text{Red payoff} = -\$10$$
$$\text{Cop payoff} = \$1$$

so now

$$\text{Blue payoff} + \text{Red payoff} + \text{Cop payoff} = \$9 - \$10 + \$1 = 0$$

which is a *three-person zero-sum* game, of sorts, where the third player has some of the characteristics of a millstone around the neck. But recall that we don't like three-person games so well as we do two-person games, because they contain the vagaries of coalitions. So non-zero-sum games offer real difficulties not present in zero-sum games, particularly if the latter are two-person games.

Parlor games, such as poker, bridge, and chess, are usually zero-sum games, and many other conflict situations may be treated as if they were. Most of the development of game theory to date has been on this type of game. Some work on non-zero-sum games has been done, and more is in progress, but the subject is beyond our scope. A troublesome case of particular interest is the two-person game in which the nominally equal payoffs differ in utility to the players; this situation occurs often even in parlor games.

STRATEGIES

Just as the word "person" has a meaning in game theory somewhat different from everyday usage, the word 'strategy' does too. This word, as used in its everyday sense, carries the connotation of a particularly skillful or adroit plan, whereas in game theory it designates any *complete* plan. *A strategy is a plan so complete that it cannot be upset by enemy action or Nature;* for everything that the enemy or Nature may choose to do, together with a set of possible actions for yourself, is just part of the description of the strategy.

So the strategy of game theory differs in two important respects from the conventional meaning: It must be utterly complete, and it may be utterly bad; for nothing is required of it except completeness. Thus, in poker, all strategies must make provision for your being dealt a royal flush in spades, and some of them will require that you fold instantly. The latter are not very glamorous strategies, but they are still strategies—after all, a bridge player once bid 7 no-trump while holding 13 spades. In a game which is completely amenable to analysis, we are able—conceptually, if not actually—to foresee all eventualities and hence are able to catalogue all possible strategies.

We are now able to mention still another criterion according to which games may be classified for study, namely, the number of strategies available to each player. Thus, if Blue and Red are the players, Blue may have three strategies and Red may have five; this would be called a 3×5 game (read 'three-by-five game').

When the number of players was discussed, you will recall that certain numbers—namely, one, two, and more-than two—were especially significant. Similarly, there are critical values in the number of strategies; and it turns out to be important to distinguish two major categories. In the first are games in which the player having the *greatest* number of strategies still has a finite number; this means that he can count them, and finish the task within some time limit. The second major category is that in which at least one player has infinitely many strategies, or, if the word 'infinitely' disturbs you, in which at least one player has a number of strategies which is larger than any definite number you can name. (This, incidentally, is just precisely what 'infinitely large' means to a mathematician.)

While infinite games (as the latter are called) cover many interesting and useful applications, the theory of such games is difficult. 'Difficult' here means that there are at least some problems the mathematician doesn't know how to solve, and further that we don't know how to present any of it within friendly pedagogical limits; such games require mathematics at the level of the calculus and beyond—mostly beyond. Therefore we here resolve to confine our attention to finite games.

THE GAME MATRIX

We are now in a position to complete the description of games, i.e., conflict situations, in the form required for game theory analysis. We will freely invoke all the restrictions developed so far. Hence our remarks will primarily apply to finite, zero-sum, two-person games.

The players are Blue and Red. Each has several potential strategies which we assume are known; let them be numbered just for identification. Blue's strategies will then bear names, such as Blue 1, Blue 2, and so on; perhaps, in a specific case, up to Blue 9; and Red's might range from Red 1 through Red 5. We would call this a nine-by-five game and write it as '9×5 game.' Just to demonstrate that it is possible to have a 9×5 game, we shall state one (or enough of it to make the point). Consider a game played on the following page.

The rules require that Blue travel from B to R, following the system of roads, without returning to B or using the same segment twice during the trip. The rules are different for Red, who must travel from R to B, always moving toward the west. Perhaps Blue doesn't want to meet Red, and has fewer inhibitions about behavior. You may verify that there are nine routes for Blue and five for Red.[1]

---

1. To avoid even the possiblity of frustrating you this early in the game,

The rules must also contain information from which we can determine what happens at the end of any play of the game: What is the payoff when, say, Blue uses the strategy Blue 7 (the northern route, perhaps) and Red uses Red 3 (the southern route, perhaps)? There will be $9 \times 5 = 45$ of these pairs and hence that number of possible values for the payoff; and these must be known. Whatever the values are, it is surely possible to arrange the information on the kind of bookkeeping form shown on Chart 1, page 188.

Such an array of boxes, each containing a payoff number, is called a *game matrix*. We shall adopt the convention that a positive number in the matrix represents a gain for Blue and hence a loss for Red, and vice versa. Thus if two of the values in the game matrix are 3 and -8, as shown in Chart 2 (page 188), the

---

we itemize the routes. Blue may visit any of the following sets of road junctions (beginning with B and ending with R in each case):

$b, bac, bacd, ab, ac, acd, dcab, dc, d$

Red may visit

b, ba, ca, cd, d

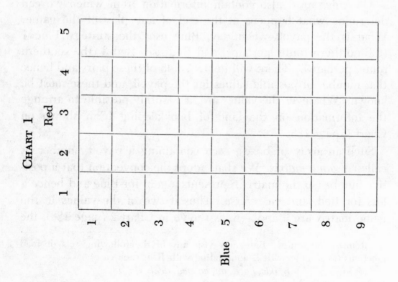

meaning is: When Blue uses Blue 6 and Red uses Red 4, Blue wins 3 units, whereas when Blue 2 is used vs. Red 2, Red wins 8 units.

When the original problem has been brought to this form, a game theory analysis may begin, for all the relevant information is represented in the descriptions of the strategies whose signatures border the matrix and in the payoff boxes. This is the game theory model of the conflict, and the applicability of the subsequent analysis will depend completely on the adequacy of this form of representation—a set of strategies and a payoff matrix.

THE CRITERION

A perennial difficulty in modelmaking of the analytical (as opposed to wooden) variety is the illness which might well be known as criterion-trouble. What is the criterion in terms of which the outcome of the game is judged? Or should be judged?

To illustrate the wealth of possible criteria in a homely example, consider a housewife who has $5 to spend on meat. What should she buy? If her criterion is simply quantity, she should buy the cheapest kind and measure the payoff in pounds. If it is variety, she should buy minimum, useful quantities of several kinds, beginning with the cheapest kinds; she measures the payoff by the number of kinds she buys. Or she may be interested in protein, fat, or calories. She may have to satisfy various side conditions, or work within certain constraints, such as allergies, tastes, or taboos. She may be interested in least total effort, in which case she may say, "I want five dollars worth of cooked meat—the nearest, of course—and deliver it sometime when you happen to be down our way."

Generally speaking, criterion-trouble is the problem of what to measure and how to base behavior on the measurements. Game Theory has nothing to say on the first topic, but it advocates a very explicit and definite behavior-pattern based on the measurements.

It takes the position that there is a definite way that rational people should behave, if they believe in the game matrix. The notion that there is some way people ought to behave does not refer to an obligation based on law or ethics. Rather it refers to a kind of mathematical morality, or at least frugality, which claims that the *sensible object of the player is to gain as much from the game as he can, safely, in the face of a skillful opponent who is pursuing an antithetical goal.* This is our model of rational behavior. As with all models, the shoe has to be tried on each time an application comes along to see whether the fit is tolerable; but it is well known in the Military Establishment, for instance, that a lot of ground can be covered in shoes that do not fit perfectly.

Let us follow up the consequences of this model in a zero-sum game, which, you will recall, is a closed system in which assets are merely passed back and forth between the players. It won't affect anything adversely (except Red), and it will simplify the discussion, if we assume for a moment that all payoffs in the game matrix are *positive;* this means that the strategy options available to the players only affect how many valuables Red must give to Blue at the end of a play of the game; this isn't a fair game for Red, but we will let him suffer for the common weal.

Now the viewpoint in game theory is that *Blue wishes to act in such a manner that the least number he can win is as great as possible, irrespective of what Red does;* this takes care of the safety requirement. *Red's comparable desire is to make the greatest number of valuables that he must relinquish as small as possible, irrespective of Blue's action.* This philosophy, if held by the players, is sufficient to specify their choices of strategy. If Blue departs from it, he does so at the risk of getting less than he might have received; and if Red departs from it, he may have to pay more than he could have settled for.

The above argument is the central one in game theory. There is a way to play every two-person game that will satisfy this criterion. However, as in the case of the housewife buying meat, it is not the only possible criterion; for example, by attributing to the enemy various degrees of ignorance or stupidity, one could devise many others. Since game theory does not attribute these attractive qualities to the enemy, it is a conservative theory.

You will note an apparent disparity in the aims of Blue and Red as stated above; Blue's aims are expressed in terms of winning and Red's in terms of losing. This difference is not a real one, as both have precisely the same philosophy. Rather, it is a consequence of our convention regarding the meaning of positive and negative numbers in the game matrix. The adoption of a uniform convention, to the effect that Blue is always the maximizing player and Red the minimizing player, will reduce technical confusion (once it becomes fixed in your mind); but let's not pay for this mnemonic by coming to believe that there is an essential lack of symmetry in the game treatment of Blue and Red.

A Note on Decision-making under Uncertainty

MARTIN SHUBIK

Martin Shubik is Professor of Industrial Administration at Yale University. This is an excerpt from his article, "Approaches to the Study of Decision-making Relevant to the Firm," which appeared in The Journal of Business *in 1961.*

By introducing considerations of probability, an attempt can be made to extend the economic theory of choice to conditions involving uncertainty. The heroic assumption must be made that the situations to be modeled are such that it is valid and useful to utilize the theory of probability. This has given rise to discussions concerning subjective probability and a large literature on probabilistic preferences and the theory of utility. Problems concerning gambling and risk preference have been examined, and several alternatives for optimal behavior have been suggested. For example, Savage has offered a man who wishes to minimize regret. In other words, after the event, when he looks back, he wishes to have acted in such a manner that he will be least sorry concerning the outcome.

Bayesian and "maximin" principles[1] have also been suggested as manners in which the individual should cope with lack of

1. [The "maximin" principle is often called the "minimax" principle. *Editor*]

knowledge. The simple examples given here illustrate the behaviors manifested in following these different principles. In Figure 1 a simple 2×2 payoff matrix is presented. The decision-maker must choose between one of two actions, knowing that "Nature," or the environment, may also make a choice which affects him. For example, if both select their second alternative, the payoff is 7 to the decision-maker. The principle he follows will depend upon his view of the forces and motivations present in his environment.

"Nature"

The Decision-maker

	1	2
1	1	9
2	2	7

FIGURE 1

The Bayesian assumption says that all the actions of "Nature" are equiprobable, and thus the optimal behavior under this assumption will be to select the first alternative, with an expected payoff of:

$$\tfrac{1}{2}\,(1) + \tfrac{1}{2}\,(9) = 5.$$

The maximin assumption has the decision-maker believe that the environment is "out to get him." In this case he will select his second alternative, assuming that, since the worst will happen, he can at least guarantee 2 for himself.

"Nature"

The Decision-maker

	1	2
1	1	0
2	0	2

FIGURE 2

The "regret payoff" is illustrated in Figure 2 for the same situation. If he selected his second alternative and the environment did likewise, he would obtain 7 (Fig. 1) but could have obtained 9 (by selecting his first alternative); hence his regret is 2.

Shackle has constructed a "potential surprise function" which he feels dominates many major decisions which must be made in face of uncertainty which cannot be adequately portrayed by considerations of probability. All the methods noted above depend upon assumptions as to how to deal with uncertainty. Which is the "best" assumption depends upon the application and knowledge of human behavior.

In spite of the limitations of models of probability, operations research and industrial statistics have, however, flourished by applying normative models of economic man acting under probabilistically portrayed uncertainty. Theoretical models of inventory, sequential sampling, and various queueing problems have been actively applied. These have already influenced the inventory levels of the whole economy and have had an effect on the understanding of reliability and risk in areas as diverse as individual credit risks, quality control in production, and stockpiling for emergency.

One area in which the applications have been fewer but the implications deeper is that of dynamic programming. This methodology deals with situations where at each period the decision-maker chooses an action which influences a sequence of events stretching off into the possibly indefinite future. In subsequent periods he has the opportunity to modify the effects of previous decisions by current action. Although this theory still deals with statistical uncertainty and mathematical expectations, the rules of decision generated as dynamic program solutions have more of the flavor of over-all long-range strategic decisions. Dividend and investment policies can be studied as dynamic programs. However, the mathematics of functional equations used in dynamic programming is, unfortunately, difficult and still relatively underdeveloped.

Introduction to Statistical
Decision Theory

JOHN PRATT, HOWARD RAIFFA, AND ROBERT SCHLAIFER

John Pratt, Howard Raiffa, and Robert Schlaifer are professors in the Graduate School of Business Administration at Harvard University. This article is taken from their book, Introduction to Statistical Decision Theory, *published in 1965.*

THE PROBLEM OF DECISION UNDER UNCERTAINTY

When all of the facts bearing on a business decision are accurately known—when the decision is made "under certainty"—careless thinking or excessive computational difficulty are the only reasons why the decision should turn out, after the fact, to have been wrong. But when the relevant facts are not all known—when the decision is made "under uncertainty"—it is impossible to make sure that every decision will turn out to have been right in this same sense. Under uncertainty, the businessman is forced, in effect, to gamble. His previous actions have put him in a position where he must place bets, hoping that he will win but knowing that he may lose. Under such circumstances, a right decision consists in the choice of the best possible bet, whether it is won or lost after the fact. A businessman who buys fire insurance does not censure himself if his plant has not burned down by the time the insurance expires, and the following example is typical of other decisions which must be made and judged in this way.

An oil wildcatter who holds an option on a plot of land in an oil-producing region must decide whether to drill on the site before the option expires or to abandon his rights. The profitability of drilling will depend on a large number of unknowns— the cost of drilling, the amount of oil or gas discovered, the price at which the oil or gas can be sold, and so forth—none of which can be predicted with certainty. His problem is further complicated by the fact that it is possible to perform various tests or experiments that will yield a certain amount of information on the geophysical structure below the land on which he has an option. Since some structures are more favorable to the existence of oil than others, this information would be of considerable help in deciding whether or not to drill; but the various tests cost a substantial amount of money, and hence it is not at all obvious that any of the available tests should be performed. The wildcatter must nevertheless decide which if any of the tests are to be performed, and ultimately, if not now, he must decide whether or not to drill.

Decision Trees · The essential characteristics of this example are two in number:
1. A *choice* or in some cases a sequence of choices must be made among various possible courses of action.
2. This choice or sequence of choices will ultimately lead to some *consequence,* but the decision maker cannot be sure in advance what this consequence will be because it depends not only on his choice or choices but on an unpredictable *event* or sequence of events.

The essence of any such problem can be brought out very clearly by a type of diagram known as a *decision tree.*

As an example that will illustrate all the essential points involved in the construction of a decision tree without useless complexities, we shall take a somewhat simplified version of the oil-drilling problem described just above. For our present purpose we shall assume that:

1. If the well is drilled at all, it will be drilled on a fixed-price contract for $100,000;

2. If oil is struck, the wildcatter will immediately sell out to a major producer for $450,000;

3. Only one type of test or experiment, namely a seismic sounding, can be performed before deciding whether or not to drill. This experiment costs $10,000; if it is performed, it will reveal with certainty whether the structure is of Type A (very favorable to the existence of oil), Type B (less favorable), or Type C (very unfavorable).

On these assumptions the wildcatter's decision problem can be represented by the tree shown as Figure 1. We imagine the decision-maker as standing at the base of the tree (the left side of the diagram) and as being obliged to choose first between having the seismic sounding made and not having it made. If the wildcatter's choice is to have the sounding made, one of three events will occur: the subsurface structure will be revealed to be of Type A, B, or C. If the wildcatter's choice is not to have the sounding made, then only one event can occur: no information.

Whatever the wildcatter's first-stage choice may be and whatever the first-stage event, the wildcatter must now enter a second stage by making a choice between drilling and abandoning the option. If he drills, then one or the other of two events will occur: oil or dry hole; if he chooses to abandon the option, the only possible "event" is "option rights lost."

Finally, at the end (right) of the tree we write down a description of the consequence of each possible sequence of choices and events. If the wildcatter chooses not to have the sounding made and to abandon his option, the consequence is simply $0—we neglect whatever he may originally have paid for the option because this is a sunk cost that cannot be affected by any present decision and therefore is irrelevant to the decision problem. Suppose, on the contrary, he decides to drill even though he has learned nothing about the subsurface structure; if he strikes a dry hole, he loses the $100,000 drilling cost, whereas if he strikes oil, his profit is the $450,000 for which he sells the rights less the $100,000 cost of drilling. If in the first stage he decides to have the sounding made, then the consequences of abandoning the option, drilling a dry hole, or striking oil are all reduced by the $10,000 cost of the sounding.

FIGURE 1

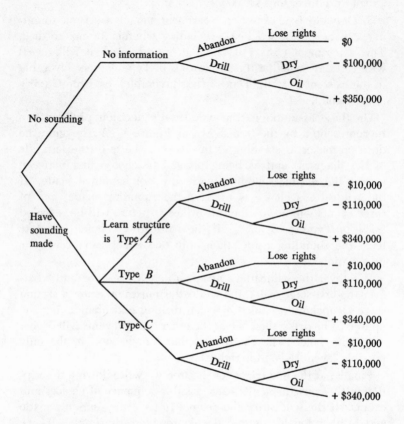

THE PROBLEM OF ANALYSIS

Analysis of the Simplest Problems · Before we even try to say what we mean by a "reasoned solution" of a complex decision problem of the kind we have just described, let us try to get a start by seeing what a sensible businessman might do when he solves a much simpler problem.

We consider an example. A manufacturer, Mr. L. K. Jones, has recently experienced a serious decline in demand for his product and as a result will be forced to lay off a substantial portion of his work force, spend money for protective treatment of idle machinery, and so forth, unless he can obtain a large order which the XYZ Company is about to place with some supplier. To have a chance at obtaining this order, Jones will have to incur considerable expense both for the making of samples and for sending a team of sales engineers to visit the XYZ Company; he must now decide whether or not to incur this expense. Formally, his problem can be described by the tree shown in Figure 2, where the three possible consequences of the two possible acts are represented by symbols:

C_1 = layoff of substantial part of work force, cost of protecting machinery;

C_2 = same as C_1, and in addition the cost of unsuccessful attempt to obtain order;

C_3 = substantial monetary profit on order, less cost of obtaining it.

FIGURE 2

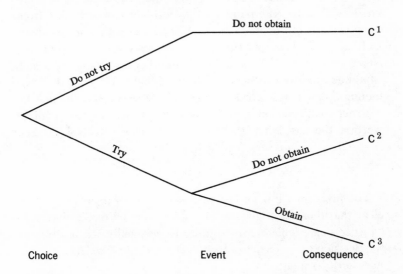

The structure of *this* problem is simple enough to make quite clear to anyone the issues that are involved in its solution. Jones (or any other sensible businessman faced with a problem of this sort) will feel that his decision will depend on two separate considerations: (1) his judgment concerning his chances of getting the order if he tries, and (2) a comparison of the cost of trying with the advantages which will accrue to him if he succeeds. If the cost is quite small relative to the advantages which would accompany success, he will make the attempt even if he thinks the chances of success are quite small; if, on the other hand, the cost of trying to get the order is so large that it would eat up most of the profits, he will not make the attempt unless he feels virtually sure that the attempt will succeed.

Sometimes a businessman who is thinking about a problem of this kind will go even further and *quantify* some if not all of his reasoning. He may say, for example, that there is so much to be gained by obtaining the order that he would try to obtain it even if there were only 1 chance in 3 of success; he may then conclude either (*a*) that he *will* make the attempt because in his opinion the chances are at least as good as 1 in 3, or else (*b*) that he *will not* make the effort because in his opinion the chances of success are less than 1 in 3. Alternatively, the businessman may start from the other side of the problem, say that in his opinion he has about 1 chance in 3 of getting the order if he tries, and then conclude either (*a*) that he *will* make the attempt because the gains which would accrue from success are so great that a 1/3 chance of obtaining them is well worth the cost of trying, or else (*b*) that he *will not* make the attempt because the gains are too small to warrant the cost when there is only 1 chance in 3 of success.

THE BASES OF DECISION: PREFERENCE AND JUDGMENT

The problem we have just discussed suffices to make it quite clear that there is in general no "objectively correct" solution to *any* decision problem. Since Jones is personally responsible for the decision to try or not to try to get the order, his decision must *necessarily* rest on:

1. How good *he feels* the chances of obtaining the order would have to be to make it worth his while to try;
2. How good *in his opinion* the chances of obtaining the order actually are.

What the businessman actually does when he answers questions of type 1 is quantify his *personal preference* for C_1 relative to C_2 and C_3; what he does when he answers questions of type 2 is quantify his *personal judgment* concerning the relative strengths of the factors that favor and oppose certain events. If he behaves reasonably, he then chooses the solution of the problem which is *consistent* with this personal preference and this personal judgment.

ANALYSIS OF COMPLEX PROBLEMS; THE ROLE OF FORMAL ANALYSIS

Since reasonable decisions in even the simplest problems must rest necessarily on the responsible decision maker's personal judgments and personal preferences, it is intuitively quite clear that these same elements must be involved in the solution of complex problems represented by decision trees with many levels and many branches at each level. It would be folly, in other words, to look for a method of analysis that will lead to an "objectively correct" solution of the oil-drilling problem we have used. A reasonable decision-maker wants his decision to agree with his preferences and his best judgments, and he will have (and should have) no use for any proposal that purports to solve his problem by some "formula" that does *not* incorporate his preferences and judgments. This assertion does not of course imply that the decision-maker should ignore objective evidence that is relevant and available.

Stated in another way, the reason why a decision-maker might want help in analyzing a decision problem like our oil-drilling example, when Jones needed no help in deciding whether or not to try for the order from the XYZ Company, is that Jones could easily see the *implications* of his preferences and judgments whereas the wildcatter cannot. The wildcatter may feel quite sure that, for example, he would decide to drill if he knew that the structure was of Type *A* or *B* and would decide not to drill if he knew that the structure was of Type *C;* however, his immediate problem is to decide whether or not to spend $10,000 in order to learn what the structure is, and while it is obvious that this information has value, it is not at all clear whether the value is greater or less than the $10,000 the information will cost.

Any decision problem, no matter how complex, can in principle be reduced to a number of problems each of which individually has the same simple structure as the problem described by the tree of Figure 2.

If, in each of these simple problems, the decision-maker will

1. Quantify his *preference* by telling us how good the chances of obtaining C_3 *would have to be* to make him willing to gamble on C_2 or C_3 rather than to take C_1 for certain, and

2. Quantify his *judgment* by telling us how good in his opinion the chances of obtaining C_3 *actually are*,

and if, in addition, he accepts certain simple principles of "reasonable," "consistent," or "coherent" behavior, then it is possible by purely logical deduction to find that solution of the complex problem which is *logically consistent with the decision-maker's own preferences and judgments*.

Naturally we are concerned with decision problems where this kind of analysis by decomposition and evaluation produces fruitful results. There are, of course, many problems—some would say "most problems"—where although in principle such an analysis could be made it would not be profitable to do so. In many situations, the incremental advantage to be gained from formal analysis cannot be expected to repay the effort, time, and cost of the analysis; in others, the decision maker may not be able, especially without training, to quantify his preference and judgments in the way required for a formal analysis; in still others, the decision problem may be faithfully abstracted into the proper form only to prove to be too complicated for the analytical tools we have available. Even after granting all these exceptions, however, there remain many problems in which formal analysis can be of considerable help to a businessman who wishes to take advantage of it.

Introduction to the Lot-size Formula

Thomson M. Whitin

Thomson M. Whitin is Professor of Economics at Wesleyan University. This is an excerpt from his article, "Inventory Control in Theory and Practice," which appeared in the Quarterly Journal of Economics *in 1952.*

The best known "scientific" inventory control system involves the calculation of economical purchase quantities and reorder point quantities. Several authors independently arrived at the same basic formula for determining economical purchase quantities in the 1920s. A number of different factors contributed to the development of such formulas.

First of all, the increasing size of business establishments has played an important role. It was possible for most firms in the past to make use of highly inefficient inventory control methods and yet still maintain profit margins. Modern large-scale enterprises often operate with small profit margins which might well be eliminated by poor inventory control methods. Furthermore, size in itself makes obvious the existence of possibilities of substantial savings through improvement in inventory control.

Secondly, during the past century, there has been an enormous increase in the amount of business training. High schools now offer some business preparatory courses, and the growth of business administration colleges has been extremely rapid. This additional training has made recent generations of businessmen more aware of improvement possibilities. Also, trade publications on market research, purchasing, retailing, standardization, and many other topics have contributed much to businessmen's understanding of the various problems which confront them.

A third factor that has aided the transition to modern inventory control methods is the increased emphasis that has been placed on the importance of engineers in business. The entrance of many trained engineers into business has brought with it the "scientific" approach, including scientific methods of production control, factory layout, standardization, etc. Also, cost accounting has helped entrepreneurs to evaluate the performance of various departments of their establishments, thus indicating specific areas where better control may be needed.

A final factor that gave impetus to research on inventory control was the "inventory depression" of 1921, which taught businessmen to be extremely wary of inventory accumulation. As a result of these factors, formulas for determining economic purchase quantities have been derived. These formulas involve a simple application of elementary differential calculus to inventory control.

The economic purchase quantity may be determined in the following manner. Two different sets of cost factors must be considered, namely, those which increase as purchase quantities increase and those which decrease as purchase quantities increase. Among those costs which increase are interest, obsolescence, risk, depreciation, storage, etc., while the forces making for decreasing costs include such items as quantity discounts, freight differentials, and procurement costs. In the following example, assume that the expense of procurement is constant and that interest, risk, depreciation, obsolescence, etc., may be lumped into one percentage figure (I). Let Y designate expected yearly sales (in \$), Q be the economic purchase quantity (in \$) and S be the procurement expense (in \$). Then total annual variable costs involved in ordering and carrying purchase quantities may be expressed as follows: $TVC = \dfrac{Q}{2}I + \dfrac{Y}{Q}S$. Differentiating with respect to the purchase quantity, Q, and setting the derivative equal to zero, the solution

$$Q = \sqrt{\frac{2YS}{I}}$$

results, where Q is the purchase quantity that minimizes combined ordering costs and carrying charges. This economical purchase quantity is thus seen to vary with the square root of sales and inversely with the square root of the carrying charges. This formula has been used in business and its use has been accompanied by good results.

Queuing Analysis and Monte Carlo Methods

William J. Baumol

William Baumol is Professor of Economics at Princeton University. This article is taken from his book, Economic Theory and Operations Analysis, published in 1961.

QUEUING ANALYSIS

Queuing theory is one of the subjects which has loomed large in the literature of operations research. Any operation in which the objects to be dealt with arrive at irregular intervals, and in which the operating facilities are of limited capacity, is a queuing problem. Automobiles waiting to be serviced in a garage, subway riders waiting to get through a turnstile, and telephone callers waiting for a clear line all constitute queues. Among the real problems to which queuing theory has been applied are the landing of aircraft, the parking of automobiles, the timing of traffic lights, the processing of films, and the servicing of travelers through customs.

One of the key characteristics of a queue is the random pattern of arrivals, which can therefore only be described in probabilistic terms. There will be times, which cannot be predicted precisely, when the number of arrivals will be unusually large, and as a result, it will then take longer to be serviced. For example, in a supermarket, customer delays at the checkout counters may be caused by the arrival of a large number of customers at the same time, or by the coincidental arrival of several customers each of whom has many groceries in her shopping basket, so that the average checkout time is materially increased.

Suppose the manager of the supermarket wishes to know what sort of delays his customers are likely to encounter. The analyst requires information about two frequency distributions, one describing customer arrivals and the other the length of time it takes a clerk to handle a customer's purchases. Once both of these have been found, mathematical analysis permits us, in many cases, to find out such things as the expected average customer waiting time, the expected length of the waiting lines at different times of the day or week, etc.

The basic idea of the calculation is relatively simple, although the details are ingenious and complicated. The probability that there will be, say, 25 customers waiting now is equal to the sum of probabilities of the several alternative series of events which can produce this result. For example, there would now be 25 customers in line if 24 customers were there one minute ago, none has since been serviced, and one more customer has just arrived. Since we know the probability of a customer's having been serviced during any one minute and of a customer's arriving during any one minute, we can find out the relationship between the probability that there were 24 customers a minute ago and the probability that there are 25 customers in line now. Similarly, we can find the probability that the lines will grow from 25 to 26 customers in this way; and we can trace, customer by customer, the expected growth of the queues in the supermarket from the time it opens in the morning with zero customers.

One of the most interesting results of the theory states, in effect, that service facilities must have excess capacity built into them if service is not to break down altogether. More specifically, suppose the service facilities, if they were always kept fully occupied, were just sufficient to meet the needs of all the store's customers. Then queues would just grow longer and longer, without limit, and ultimately the operations would collapse. The basic reason for this result is, of course, that customer arrivals are *not* spread evenly in time, and so during some periods the facility will temporarily be idle whereas at other times it will be overcrowded. But, by assumption, the facilities would be of sufficient capacity only if there were no such oscillations in customer arrival time. To permit them to cope with bunched arrivals, therefore, the capacity of service facilities must be increased.

The theory also permits us, at least in principle, to investigate how much the expected length of queue lines will be reduced when a number of new checkout counters are added in our supermarket. This immediately raises an optimality question— just how many checkout counters should the supermarket have? More counters cost money to install and operate. Too many counters will therefore be wasteful, but too small a number of counters will slow down service and lose customers. The optimality problem, then, is to determine the intermediate number of counters which best serves management's purposes. Unfortunately, these probabilistic optimality calculations are often likely to grow very complex; therefore, instead of a direct approach to the problem, the operations researcher frequently resorts to the methods described in the following section.

ARTIFICIAL EXPERIMENTATION: MONTE CARLO TECHNIQUES

Before we can hope to find out the consequences of a course of action, it is necessary to have some sort of data. For example, suppose, as before, that it is desired to test some proposed service facilities to see how often customers will be kept waiting, and how long they will have to wait, on the average. These figures, of course, depend on the fluctuations in the number of customer arrivals—how frequently their number will exceed a particular magnitude.

In solving such a problem, experimentation is not a real possibility. It can be costly in customer relations to try very much more meager service facilities just to see what will happen. It may be that some information can be obtained from the experience of other supermarkets. But this may be too limited in range and in quantity to be of much assistance.

The operations researcher has, however, invented another very effective way to gather the relevant data: that is, to make them up himself, or rather to let the mathematical statistician make them up for him! But one may well ask, how can improvised statistics help us to foresee what will happen in the real world?

The answer is that the numbers are invented in a manner which carefully employs the analytical methods of mathematical statistics in order to stretch as far as possible such few actual data as are available to begin with. At some particular moment in the week we may assume that customers will arrive randomly, in a pattern somewhat similar to outcomes in successive throws of a pair of dice. The pattern of customer arrivals may then be described in terms of a frequency distribution, which indicates how many weeks in a year customer arrivals per hour can be expected to fall between 100 and 110 units, how often the number will lie in the 110 to 120 range, etc.

Now, from the available information *and the nature of the problem*, the statistician can often decide which frequency distribution best describes the pattern of expected customer arrivals. From this frequency distribution it is then possible to construct an artificial history of customer arrivals by choosing randomly among all the possibilities, but in a way which is "loaded" to produce the right frequencies. To give a very simple illustration, suppose we consider two possibilities: *A*, fewer than 100 arrivals per hour and *B*, at least 100 arrivals. If, on some basis, the odds are computed to be 2 to 1 in favor of *A*, we can generate an artificial demand history as follows: Toss the (unbiased) die. If it falls, 1, 2, 3, or 4, put down an *A*; if it falls 5 or 6, put down a *B*. This might yield a pattern for weekly demands such as the following:

TABLE 1

"Week"	Face of die	Arrival "history"	
		Under 100	100 or more
First	3	A	
Second	1	A	
Third	3	A	
Fourth	5		B
Fifth	6		B
Sixth	2	A	
Seventh	2	A	

This, incidentally, indicates the reason for the term "Monte Carlo method."

In practice, it is not actually necessary to toss any dice. Instead, we can use tables called "tables of random numbers" which have been worked out in advance. Moreover, the computations can be made by high-speed electronic computers which are able, in a few minutes or hours, to run off thousands of cases and manufacture data whose collection would, otherwise, require many years. But although this method is economical and powerful, it must be used only with the greatest care and caution. As we have seen, everything depends on the choice of frequency distribution (i.e., the odds of the various outcomes), and unless there is some assurance that these have been picked well, the entire calculation can be worthless.

Once this artificial experience has been generated, it can be used to find approximate solutions to optimality problems such as that of determining the number of checkout counters which was described in the last section—problems where straightforward computational methods are too complex. To illustrate the approach, consider the (unrelated) problem of finding an approximate root of the equation

$$X^2 - 6X + 9.1 = 0.$$

Instead of using the standard formula, we can go about it indirectly by trial and error, first, say, substituting $X = 1$ to find that the expression takes the value

$$(1)^2 - 6(1) + 9.1 = 4.1.$$

Clearly, $X = 1$ is not our root. So we try again, this time using, say, $X = 0$, and we see that this value of X makes the expression equal 9.1—i.e., it has only made things worse. We therefore infer that we have been going in the wrong direction, so this time we go up and try $X = 2$, etc. The results of several such trials can be tabulated as follows:

Trial value of X	1	0	2	3	4
Value of $X^2 - 6X + 9.1$	4.1	9.1	1.1	0.1	1.1

Clearly, this suggests that there is a root located very close to $X = 3$, at which the value of the expression is very close to zero, and we can take this as the approximate value of the root we are seeking.

The finding of optimal solutions in queuing problems and many other difficult operations problems can be approached in somewhat the same spirit with the aid of Monte Carlo methods. A number of alternative possibilities (number of possible checkout counters) can be postulated, and their consequences over a long period can then be simulated and reported on by the computer with the aid of Monte Carlo predictions of customer arrivals. If our objective is to minimize some sort of over-all cost function (which includes the costs of operating additional checkout counters as well as the costs of customer delays), we would take the optimal solution to be approximated by that trial (number of checkout counters) for which the machine reported the lowest over-all expected costs.

Unfortunately, this description, although correct in essence, is somewhat misleading in its simplicity. Particularly where decisions involve the assignment of values to a number of interrelated variables and where the ranges of possible values are considerable, there are difficult problems in deciding on what combination of values to try out next. It is by no means easy to design a procedure which converges with reasonable rapidity toward an optimal solution.

It is to be emphasized that the use of Monte Carlo methods is not limited to queuing problems. They can be used in inventory analysis, replacement analysis (when to stop repairing a piece of equipment and replace it with a new one), and a wide variety of other situations in which a prominent role is played by probabilistic elements such as the timing and magnitudes of customer demands or of the need for repairs.

Part Four

Application of Operations Research to Military Planning and the Role of the Computer in Industrial Management

MODERN economic analysis and operations research have become extremely important in the Department of Defense, particularly during the tenure of Robert McNamara, a Ford Motor Company executive and a former professor of business administration, as Secretary of Defense. The first three papers in Part Four attempt to show how these techniques can be, and are being, applied to problems of high-level military planning. Charles Hitch and Ronald N. McKean describe the elements of a military problem of economic choice and show that two frequently used approaches to these problems suffer from important defects, an application of elementary economic principles yielding more satisfactory results. The short article by Merton J. Peck and Frederick M. Scherer suggests how cost-effectiveness analysis can be used to estimate the value of a weapons system. The article from *Fortune* is a case study of the impact of operations research—or systems analysis, as it is sometimes called—on airlift and sea-lift capabilities.

The electronic computer has had an enormous impact on management practices, and its full influence has yet to be felt. The computer allows the manager to control the firm and assess its environment with new effectiveness because it enables him to get the relevant facts quickly and to understand their changing relationships. The last three papers in Part Four are concerned with the role of the computer in industrial management. The article from *Fortune* describes the Westinghouse Electric Corporation's use of computers, both to reduce the length of time required to obtain management information and to simulate various aspects of its business.

Harold Leavitt and Thomas Whisler try to predict the impact of the electronic computer on managerial organization. In their judgment, the boundary between planning and performance will move upward, and there will be a tendency toward recentralization and a radical reorganization of middle management. Herbert Simon is also concerned with the changes that will take place in the job of the manager during the next generation. He concludes that "the change in occupational profile depends on a well-known economic principle, the doctrine of comparative advantage. . . . [Thus,] if computers are a hundred times faster than executives in making investment decisions, but only ten times faster in handling employee grievances (the quality of the decisions being held constant), then computers will be employed in making investment decisions, while executives will be employed in handling grievances."

Economic Choice in Military Planning

CHARLES J. HITCH AND
RONALD N. McKEAN

Charles Hitch was Assistant Secretary of Defense until 1965, when he became Vice President of the University of California. Roland McKean is Professor of Economics at the University of California at Los Angeles. This paper comes from their book, The Economics of Defense in the Nuclear Age, *published in 1960.*

THE ELEMENTS OF AN ECONOMIC ANALYSIS

The essence of economic choice in military planning is not quantitative analysis: calculation may or may not be necessary or useful, depending upon the problem and what is known about it. The essential thing is the comparison of all the relevant alternatives from the point of view of the objectives each can accomplish and the costs which it involves; and the selection of the best (or a "good") alternative through the use of appropriate economic criteria.

The elements of a military problem of economic choice, whether its solution requires advanced mathematics, high speed computing equipment, or just straight hard thinking, are therefore the following:

215

1. An objective or objectives. What military (or other national) aim or aims are we trying to accomplish with the forces, equipments, projects, or tactics that the analysis is designed to compare? Choice of objectives is fundamental: if it is wrongly made, the whole analysis is addressed to the wrong question.

2. Alternatives. By what alternative forces, equipments, projects, tactics, and so on, may the objective be accomplished? The alternatives are frequently referred to as *systems*[1] because each combines all the elements—men, machines, and the tactics of their employment—needed to accomplish the objective. System A may differ from System B in only one respect (for example, in number of bombs per bomber), or in several (number of bombs per bomber, number of strikes, and so on), but both are complete systems, however many elements they have in common. The great problem in choosing alternatives to compare is to be sure that all the good alternatives have been included. Frequently we lack the imagination to do this at the beginning of an analysis; we think of better alternatives (that is, invent new systems) as the analysis proceeds and we learn more about the problem. The invention of new and better systems in this fashion is indeed one of the principal payoffs from this kind of analysis.

3. Costs or resources used. Each alternative method of accomplishing the objective, or in other words each system, involves the incurring of certain costs or the using up of certain resources (these are different phrases to describe the same phenomena). Costs are the negative values in the analysis (as the objectives are positive values). The resources required may be general (as is commonly the case in problems of long-range planning), or highly specific (as in most tactical problems), or mixed.

4. A model or models. Models are abstract representations of reality which help us to perceive significant relations in the real world, to manipulate them, and thereby predict others. They may take any of numerous forms. Some are small-scale physical representations of reality, like model aircraft in a wind tunnel. Many are simply representations on paper—like mathematical models. Or, finally, they may be simple sets of relationships that are sketched out in the mind and not formally put down on paper.

---

1. Hence "systems analysis," a term frequently applied to complex quantitative analyses.

In no case are models photographic reproductions of reality; if they were, they would be so complicated that they would be of no use to us. They have to abstract from a great deal of the real world—focusing upon what is relevant for the problem at hand, ignoring what is irrelevant. Whether or not one model is better than another depends not on its complexity, or its appearance of reality, but solely on whether it gives better predictions (and thereby helps us to make better decisions).[2] In systems analyses models of one type or another are required to trace the relations between inputs and outputs, resources and objectives, for each of the systems to be compared, so that we can predict the relevant consequences of choosing any system.

5. A criterion. By "criterion" we mean the test by which we choose one alternative or system rather than another. The choice of an appropriate economic criterion is frequently the central problem in designing a systems analysis. In principle, the criterion we want is clear enough: the optimal system is the one which yields the greatest excess of positive values (objectives) over negative values (resources used up, or costs). But as we have already seen, this clear-cut ideal solution is seldom a practical possibility in military problems.[3] Objectives and costs usually have no common measure: there is no generally acceptable way to subtract dollars spent or aircraft lost from enemy targets destroyed. Moreover, there may be multiple objectives or multiple costs that are incommensurable. So in most military analyses we have to be satisfied with some approximation to the ideal criterion that will enable us to say, not that some system A is optimal, but that it is better than some other proposed systems B, C, and so on. In many cases we will have to be content with calculating efficient rather than optimal systems, relying on the intuitive judgment of well-informed people (of whom the analyst may be one) to

2. Bombardiers once bombed visually, using simple models in their heads to estimate the bomb's trajectory in relation to the target. Modern bombsights use mathematical models, requiring high speed computers for solution, to make the same estimate. The model used by the modern bombsight is better only if its predictions are more accurate—a question of fact which has to be tested by experiment.

3. In private industry this "ideal" criterion is the familiar one of profit maximization.

select one of the efficient systems in the neighborhood of the optimum.

It cannot be stated too frequently or emphasized enough that economic choice is *a way of looking at problems* and does not necessarily depend upon the use of any analytic aids or computational devices. Some analytic aids (mathematical models) and computing machinery are quite likely to be useful in analyzing complex military problems, but there are many military problems in which they have not proved particularly useful where, nevertheless, it is rewarding to array the alternatives and think through their implications in terms of objectives and costs. Where mathematical models and computations are useful, they are in no sense alternatives to or rivals of good intuitive judgment; they supplement and complement it. Judgment is always of critical importance in designing the analysis, choosing the alternatives to be compared, and selecting the criterion. Except where there is a completely satisfactory one-dimensional measurable objective (a rare circumstance), judgment must supplement the quantitative analysis before a choice can be recommended.

THE REQUIREMENTS APPROACH

In the absence of systematic analysis in terms of objectives and costs, a procedure that might be called the "requirements approach" is commonly used in the military departments and throughout much of the government. Staff officers inspect a problem, say, the defense of the continental United States or the design of the next generation of heavy bomber, draft a plan which seems to solve the problem, and determine requirements from the plan. Then feasibility is checked: Can the "required" performance characteristics, such as some designated speed and range, be achieved? Can the necessary budget be obtained? Does the nation have the necessary resources in total? If the program passes the feasibility tests, it is adopted; if it fails, some adjustments have to be made. But the question: What are the payoffs *and the costs* of alternative programs? may not be explicitly asked during the process of setting the requirement or deciding upon the budget. In fact, officials have on occasion boasted that their stated "requirements" have been based on need alone.

This, of course, is an illusion. Some notion of cost (money, resources, time), however imprecise, is implicit in the recognition of any limitation. Military departments frequently determine "requirements" which are from 10 to 25 percent higher than the available budget, but never ten times as high, and seldom twice as high. But this notion of cost merely rules out grossly infeasible programs. It does not help in making optimal or efficient choices.

For that purpose it is essential that alternative ways of achieving military objectives be costed, and that choices be made on the basis of payoff and cost. How *are* choices made by military planners prior to any costing of alternatives? We have never heard any satisfying explanation. The derivation of requirements by any process that fails to cost alternatives can result in good solutions only by accident. Probably military planners sometimes weigh relative costs in some crude manner, at least subconsciously, even when they deny they do; or they make choices on the basis of considerations which ought to be secondary or tertiary, such as the preservation of an existing command structure, or the matching of a reported foreign accomplishment.

The defects of the requirements approach can be seen clearly if we think of applying it to our problems as a consumer. Suppose the consumer mulls over his transportation problem and decides, "on the basis of need alone," that he requires a new Cadillac. It is "the best" car he knows, and besides Jones drives one. So he buys a Cadillac, ignoring cost and ignoring therefore the sacrifices he is making in other directions by buying "the best." There are numerous alternative ways of solving the consumer's transportation problem (as there are always numerous ways of solving a military problem), and a little costing of alternatives prior to purchase might have revealed that the purchase of "the best" instrument is not *necessarily* an optimal choice. Perhaps if the consumer had purchased a Pontiac or a secondhand Cadillac he would have saved enough to maintain and operate it and take an occasional trip.[4] Or if he had purchased a Chevrolet he could have afforded to keep his old car and become head of a two-car family. One of these alternatives, properly costed and compared,

4. Costing in our sense is never simply the cost of a unit of equipment; it is always the cost of a complete system including everything that must be purchased with the equipment and the cost of maintaining and operating it.

might have promised a far greater amount of utility for the consumer than the purchase of a new Cadillac "on the basis of need alone." Or the exercise might have reassured the consumer that the new Cadillac was indeed optimal. While expensive unit equipment is not necessarily optimal, in some cases it can be proved to be.

THE PRIORITIES APPROACH

Another procedure that seems to have a great deal of appeal, in both military planning and other government activities, is the "priorities approach." To facilitate a decision about how to spend a specified budget, the desirable items are ranked according to the urgency with which they are needed. The result is a list of things that might be bought, the ones that are more important being near the top and the ones that are less important being near the bottom. Lists that rank several hundred weapons and items have sometimes been generated in the military services.

At first blush, this appears to be a commendable and systematic way to tackle the problem. When one reflects a bit, however, the usefulness and significance of such a list begins to evaporate. Consider the following items ranked according to their (hypothetical) priorities: (1) Missile X, (2) Radar device Y, (3) Cargo aircraft Z. How do you use such a ranking? Does it mean that the entire budget should be spent on the first item? Probably not, for it is usually foolish to allocate all of a budget to a single weapon or object. Besides, if a budget is to be so allocated, the ranking of the items below the first one has no significance.

Does the ranking mean that the money should go to the first item until no additional amount is needed, then to the second item until no further amount is needed, and so on? Hardly, because there could be some need for more of Missile X almost without limit. Even if only a limited amount of Missile X was available, to keep buying right out to this limit would usually be a foolish rule. After quite a few Missile X's were purchased, the next dollar could better be spent on some other item. Even using lifeboats for women and children first is foolish if a sailor or doctor on each lifeboat can save many lives.

Perhaps a priority list means that we should spend more money on the higher-priority items than on those having a lower priority.

But this makes little sense, since some of the items high on the list, for example, the radar device, may cost little per unit and call at most for a relatively small amount of money; while some lower-ranking purchases, such as the cargo aircraft, may call for comparatively large sums if they are to be purchased at all. In any event, the priorities reveal nothing about how much more should be spent on particular items.

Just how anyone can use such a list is not clear. Suppose a consumer lists possible items for his monthly budget in the order of their priority and he feels that in some sense they rank as follows: (1) groceries, (2) gas and oil, (3) cigarettes, (4) repairs to house, (5) liquor, and (6) steam baths. This does not mean that he will spend all of his funds on groceries, nor does it mean that he will spend nothing on liquor or steam baths. His problem is really to allocate his budget among these different objects. He would like to choose the allocation such that an extra dollar on cigarettes is just as important to him as an extra dollar on groceries. At the margin, therefore, the objects of expenditure would be equally important (except for those that are not purchased at all).

The notion of priority stems from the very sensible proposition that one should do "first things first." It makes sense, or at least the top priority does, when one considers the use of a small increment of resources or time. If one thinks about the use of an extra dollar or of the next half-hour of his time, it is sensible to ask, "What is the most urgent—the first-priority—item?" If one is deciding what to do with a budget or with the next eight hours, however, he ordinarily faces a problem of *allocation*, not of setting priorities. A list of priorities does not face the problem or help solve it.

Thus in formulating defense policy and choosing weapon systems, we have to decide how much effort or how many resources should go to each item. The "priorities approach" does not solve the allocation problem and can even trap us into adopting foolish policies.[5]

5. For a revealing discussion of priority lists, see *Military Construction Appropriations for 1958,* Hearings before the Subcommittee of the Committee on Appropriations, House of Representatives, 85th Congress, 1st Session, U.S. Government Printing Office, Washington, D.C., 1957, pp. 420-427.

The Value of a Weapon System and Cost-effectiveness Analysis

MERTON J. PECK AND
FREDERICK M. SCHERER

Merton J. Peck is Professor of Economics at Yale University. Frederick M. Scherer is Assistant Professor of Economics at Princeton University. This short piece comes from their book, The Weapons Acquisition Process, *which appeared in 1962.*

The contribution of a weapon system to the prosecution of warfare can be considered in two general cases. For defensive weapons military value is the damage avoided to the defending nation's cities and armed forces that enemy weapons would otherwise perpetrate, both because this damage would make the postwar situation less tolerable and because avoiding damage increases the chances of successfully prosecuting the war.[1] For offensive systems military value depends upon the damage done to an enemy's cities, military installations, and economy. In this case military

1. The military value measurements here can be assumed to be in terms of physical resource opportunity costs. For purposes of the present illustration, there is nothing to be gained by jumping into the controversy over how the economic value of a human life is to be ascertained.

value derives not from the damage itself, but from the effect the damage has on shortening or ending the war on favorable terms.[2]

To be sure, this notion of quantifying military value is decidedly nonoperational, given the present state of economic analysis in the weapon systems sphere. It is possible that direct methods for estimating the value of weapon systems might be developed. Such a step would be most significant, as Oskar Morgenstern argues:

> To develop a method (for determining military worth) would be more important than to introduce some further, purely technological, advances in some weapon system. It would improve the use of all of these.[3]

Nevertheless, even if efforts in this direction should prove fruitless, the methodology known as cost-effectiveness analysis provides in some cases an operational substitute for direct value measurements, given only certain decisions on broad military objectives. Thus, if a decision is made on the number and types of enemy targets to be destroyed if war breaks out or on the number of attacking aircraft or missiles to be intercepted, it is possible through cost-effectiveness techniques to estimate the incremental savings which a proposed new weapon system would afford over existing or alternative methods of accomplishing the objective. For example, cost-effectiveness analysis undoubtedly would show that a force of Polaris weapon systems provides substantial cost savings over a force of B-47's capable of inflicting the same amount of retaliatory damage, given the attrition rates expected for B-47's at the hands of enemy antiaircraft defenses and the vulnerability of manned bombers on the ground to surprise attack. Such savings reflect the incremental military value of the program under consideration, as long as the objective is held constant. It would appear that this approach, which essentially measures opportunity costs or avoidable costs, is a tolerable surrogate for military value estimates in development cost-quality tradeoff decisions, although it is probably less satisfactory in cost-time tradeoff situations.

2. The direct value of damage to an enemy's homeland may even be negative. As in World War II, the victor might later find it to his advantage to help repair the damage he has done, or the vanquished might have to pay reparations.
3. *The Question of National Defense* (New York: Random House, 1959), p. 205.

Systems Analysis by Land,
Sea, and Air

FORTUNE MAGAZINE

*This article appeared in the July 1965 issue
of* Fortune *Magazine. It is an interesting
case study of the impact of operations research on airlift and sealift capabilities.*

One of the first things Robert S. McNamara made clear when
he took office [as Secretary of Defense] was that he wanted more
airlift capability, and soon. He turned to a group working under
Alain Enthoven, his Deputy Assistant Secretary for Systems Analysis, with a relatively simple question: How many more transports should the Defense Department be ordering?

The only modern transports then in production were the Lockheed C-130E, an extended-range turboprop that was able to take
off and land on short runways, was easy to load from trucks, and
could be used in air drops—but had a relatively small payload;
and the Boeing C-135, a pure jet that was larger and faster, but
required well-developed landing fields. The decision was to buy
forty-nine more C-130E's and thirty more C-135's than had been
originally programed for fiscal 1962. However, the analysis that
went into this decision was fast and, by current standards, loose.

The next sequence of questions concerned the aircraft intended
to be a successor to these two, the Lockheed C-141. The C-141
had more range and speed than either of the others, could carry

over 50,000 pounds, and could take off or land on 5,000-foot run-ways. It had been hailed as a triumph of modern airlift technology, and there was no doubt that it was a lot better than anything then available. Yet McNamara immediately began questioning its adequacy for the missions it was likely to perform; and in response to a long series of questions from his office, the analysts turned up some problems about the C-141. One difficulty was the fact that the plane simply could not handle many pieces of outsize equipment; its configuration prevented it from carrying radars and large trucks, for example, that could be easily loaded on other aircraft, like the Douglas C-133. This equipment could be dispensed with by light airborne divisions, but not by the heavy infantry divisions implied in McNamara's view of U.S. limited-war needs. All in all, he discovered in mid-1961, perhaps a third of the equipment carried by an infantry division could not fit into the C-141. In addition, there was a kind of "mismatch" between its cubic capacity and its weight capacity—i.e., when it carried any likely assortment of military cargo its space would be filled long before it was carrying the tonnage it was designed to lift. McNamara asked for a study to ascertain how long the plane's development would be delayed by a decision to remedy this imbalance. The answer was at least a year, possibly two—which was too long—and besides, the remedy would involve some reductions in the plane's performance. Accordingly, McNamara agreed to go ahead with engineering development of the C-141. It was test-flown in December, 1963, and began coming into service on schedule the next spring.

By the fall of 1961 it was clear that "rapid deployment" was to be a continuing object of analysis. With the buildup of the C-130E's and the C-135's continuing, and the C-141 on the way, the analysts were asked to find the "mix" that would produce the most effective force. This, in turn, got them deep into a study of the missions that might be required of the aircraft; and the study got them interested, not only in more efficient aircraft, but in *alternatives* to aircraft. There were two main alternatives, pre-positioning equipment on land overseas—e.g., in Thailand—and pre-positioning aboard ships overseas.

The idea of stockpiling on land was not itself new, of course, but it had never previously been viewed systematically in relation to airlift problems. To some extent, the new interest in pre-positioning on land arose out of the C-141's problems. It occurred to some analysts that many of the bulky items that could not be carried on the plane were relatively inexpensive and easy to maintain; thus it would be economical to stock them abroad, and accept the prospect that many of them would be "wasted," i.e., in the wrong place at the wrong time, instead of trying to fly all of them to the right place at the right time.

The use of ships to pre-position equipment abroad was a more novel concept. It was first developed, not by the Pentagon's in-house analysts, but by an outside consultant, Planning Research Corporation. Specifically, the proposal was that equipment be loaded on rehabilitated Victory ships, which could be stationed overseas at a number of strategic locations. McNamara bought this idea of the "forward floating depot," and there are now three ships in service, docked around Subic Bay in the Philippines.

The increased interest in pre-positioning was one reason for the Air Force's failure to sell McNamara on a new outsize-cargo plane. By the spring of 1963 the old C-133's, which had been handling the biggest items in the Army's inventory (they had originally been designed to carry Atlas and Titan missiles), were having severe maintenance problems. McNamara insisted that any successor had to be able to do more than just move outsize cargo. He told the Air Force that he might be receptive to a new plane, but that it would have to compete on a cost-effectiveness basis with pre-positioning.

Both the Air Force and Enthoven's systems analysts, meanwhile, had begun to think seriously of a plane that would be very competitive indeed—a plane that could be used efficiently to transport all the men and equipment of any division, and that could deliver them far forward in the battle area. Design studies on such a plane were accelerated by the Air Force and by Boeing, Douglas, and Lockheed, and by the fall of 1963 work had crystallized in some radical new design proposals. The proposals were exciting: when it was operational, the proposed plane would be three times as productive as the C-141 and only 50 percent more expensive to operate. It would be far better balanced for weight and space than the C-141, and could take off and land on runways that were then considered suitable only for light twin-engine aircraft. And it was a "state-of-the-art" plane—i.e., no scientific breakthroughs were required to build it—although development costs would nevertheless be expensive.

In a sense, the question about this plane was a simple one: Was it worth paying the development costs to get the operational efficiencies? But efforts to answer this question led to some others that were complex. The development costs were clearly not worth paying unless our airlift requirements were larger than then estimated. How much larger did they have to be? A group of rapid-deployment analysts in Enthoven's office, led by John Keller, established that the "breakeven point" was an extra 20,000 tons— i.e., if we needed the capability to lift these to any point in the world within thirty days, then the operating efficiencies would serve to amortize the development costs within the life of the plane. Keller's group thought that there was a good case for a substantially greater requirement. In the fall of 1963 they laid their figures before McNamara, expecting that he would want to push ahead on the new plane.

Instead, he questioned the assumption that requirements would, in fact, be rising very sharply. Was a lot more rapid deployment really called for by the strategies that we were likely to adopt in crises? At a certain cost level, might it be desirable to settle for a slower response? In effect, McNamara was raising a question about the dollar value of the proposed new capabilities. "You can always go faster and heavier at a price," Keller commented recently, in recalling this issue. "But at some point you begin to run out of benefits and you're spending money as though it were going out of style."

To get a fix on the value of additional rapid deployment, McNamara requested an analysis by the Joint Chiefs of Staff. The Joint Chiefs turned to their Special Studies Group, a team of military systems analysts that had been organized in 1962 to study military problems for them and the Secretary. The study group was asked to examine rapid-deployment requirements in three different areas of the world—Korea, Southeast Asia, and Iran— with three different possible strategies applied in each: (1) a "forward" strategy, emphasizing a capability to get fully equipped fighting men into action within a few days; (2) a "defensive" strategy that assumed we did not need an immediate capability to do more than gain a toehold, and that we would build up our forces slowly and fight the crucial battles in a month or more; and (3) an intermediate strategy, assuming a capability somewhere in between the first two. The forward strategy, of course, required the most rapid deployment, the defensive strategy the least.

The study group's report, delivered in July 1964, is regarded in the Pentagon today as a landmark in systems analysis. It related the heavy costs involved in rapidly deploying fully equipped men to the economies involved in ending wars sooner—in not having to call up the reserves, for example. The report established overwhelmingly that the big costs, both in dollars and in casualties, are those arising out of prolonged conflicts. The forward strategy was by far the most economical of the three; when all were successful, its edge over the defensive strategy was put at more than $10 billion, and its edge even over the intermediate strategy was substantial. Which meant, of course, that rapid deployment was an exceedingly good buy, and worth buying in large chunks.

Meanwhile, the Air Force and the manufacturers had gone back to the drawing board and come up with an aircraft of sharply improved cost effectiveness. When the results of both efforts were put before McNamara, he recommended an immediate go-ahead to the President. Present indications are that the plane will have a takeoff weight of 725,000 pounds (versus 316,000 pounds for the C-141) and will operate at a very high level of efficiency (at least 40 percent cheaper than the C-141). The plane is now known as the C-5A, and the Pentagon's plan is to spend something over $2 billion to get a "modest force" in operation by the early 1970's.

Meanwhile, the Navy's interest in rapid deployment has grown. The final product of several different studies in the Navy, some initiated by systems analysts within the service and some undertaken at McNamara's request, has been a fast-deployment logistics ship, now called FDL, which represents an extraordinary advance over the original forward floating depot. It will be fast, probably around twenty-four knots, and will be powered by an aircraft-type gas-turbine engine. In ports it will quickly "roll on" and "roll off" 5,000 tons of Army equipment; it will also be able to put its cargo over-the-beach with its own amphibian vehicles if necessary. What is most interesting about it, though, is that it is designed to move about on the open seas, as a forward *mobile* depot—which means that the chances of its being trapped in a port are minimized, and also means that it can set off for a potential trouble zone without triggering an international crisis. Eventually several dozen or so of the ships may be in operation.

Obviously, both the Air Force and the Navy are in rapid deployment to stay.

"On Line" in "Real Time"

GILBERT BURCK

This article appeared in the April 1964 issue of Fortune. *Its author, Gilbert Burck, is an editor of that magazine.*

Members of Westinghouse Electric Corporation's executive committee recently filed into a small room in the company's new Tele-Computer Center near Pittsburgh and prepared to look at their business as no group of executives had ever looked at business before. In front of them was a large video screen, and to one side of the screen was a "remote inquiry" device that seemed a cross between a typewriter and a calculator. As the lights dimmed, the screen lit up with current reports from many of the company's important divisions—news of gross sales, orders, profitability, inventory levels, manufacturing costs, and various measures of performance based on such data. When the officers asked the remote-inquiry device for additional information or calculations, distant computers shot back the answers in seconds.

This was only an experimental performance, designed to show how the corporation's decision makers could someday be provided with practically all the timely and relevant information they need to run the company. No computer system can do that yet, and a few academicians doubt that such a system will ever do it. But top managers in companies like Westinghouse are enthusiastically supporting the efforts of their systems men to convert common business data into useful knowledge with the computer.

The computer is making such rapid, continuous progress in converting knowledge into efficiency and dollar savings that no man can yet be sure of its potential.

Knowledge is power and control, provided it is timely, ample, and relevant. Only a businessman who knows what is happening inside his company as soon as it happens can truly adjust his means to his aims; and only one who understands what is happening in the marketplace as soon as it happens can really make sound decisions about his aims. But even a lot of timely facts is not enough. Most facts are either dead the moment they are born, or are the remnants of autopsies on history. Unless a man understands how they are related, and particularly how their relationships are changing, he knows very little.

Today's advanced electronic computer enables a man to control his business and to assess its environment with incomparable effectiveness because it enables him both to lay hands on relevant facts swiftly and to understand their changing relationships. Besides supplying him with facts in historical time, or after they have happened, it supplies him with facts "on line," i.e., as soon as they are born, and in "real time," i.e., promptly and abundantly enough to control the circumstances they describe while those circumstances are developing. The computer helps the businessman understand the changing relationships of facts chiefly by a technique known as simulation, or the imitation of experience with models. Without the computer, he must build many models and compare them laboriously, or even construct pilot plants, and both methods cost much time and money. With the computer he needs only to translate an appropriate number of models into mathematical formulas and instruct the computer to compare them and pick the likeliest. He can also simulate part or all of his operation in a computer, and test it in dozens of different situations.

The simulation technique grows in effectiveness when a corporation can repeatedly inspect its past performance and gauge its objectives accordingly—that is, after the business has become "computerized," and the records of its "transactions" over the years have been stored in the machine's memory. Given such a "continuum" of information, the businessman can keep on refining his model by taking it apart, nailing down its variables, rejiggering its weights. As time passes, his model gets better and better, and he can make millions of telling comparisons in a few minutes. He knows precisely what has happened and why, what should be happening and why, and he has an excellent notion of what is likely to happen, and what is the best way of capitalizing on it all. He can rely less and less on guesses and hunch and more and more on analysis. As somebody once remarked hyperbolically, an executive is a genius if he is right fifty-two percent of the time. Whatever the correct percentage, computer men argue, the machine can help him expand and elevate his native intuitive powers to new levels.

The vast bulk of United States businesses' fourteen thousand computer installations are still confined to routine data processing —preparing payrolls and paychecks for nearly every kind of business, recording and sorting bank checks, making out bills for telephone and electric utilities, analyzing personnel data, preparing financial results for corporate annual reports, and performing all manner of scientific calculations. But now that the practicality of real-time applications has been demonstrated, more and more corporations are starting the arduous process of putting themselves at least partly on real time lest competitors get the jump on them. By 1970, computer sages predict, nearly all new electronic data-processing systems will be on line in real time.

Westinghouse Electric Corporation is said to use computers in a wider range of applications than any other United States company; whether it does or not, it has a clear notion of what it wants to do with them. The aim of the company's business-systems department, says Lou Hague, its director, is to shrink the lead time in the management information cycle to practically nothing, and eventually to be able to prepare a final report that will include just about everything top management needs to make its decisions. Some are skeptical. John Dearden of the Harvard Business School argues that flooding high-level management with operational information is "sheer nonsense." But Hague points out that no competent computer-system man proposes to inundate managers with useless information, and anyway no good top manager would stand for it. The phrase for what he and other systems men want to present to managers is "exception information," or information that calls for attention and action.

How the computer monitors exception information is illustrated by an example the business-systems department uses for internal education. Costs in a certain plant have been normal for a while, but begin to rise steeply. Without the computer, these costs would get far out of line before being noticed, and would not be brought back for a week or more; but with real-time control they get only a little out of line before being noticed, and are brought back promptly. The cumulative effect on profits can be enormous.

Westinghouse's business-systems department is tackling one problem at a time; Hague says it doesn't yet know enough to do the job all at once, and he doubts that anyone else does. And the company keeps expansion within realistic limits by making computer operations pay off in identifiable savings. Last year Westinghouse spent $16,200,000 for machine rentals and programing and research. But it realized $20,700,000 and thus saved $4,500,000 or nearly 30 percent on its outlays, not including indirect benefits such as better customer service and improved cash flow.

Westinghouse's adventure with the computer began seven years ago, when Hague hired James Emery, now teaching production and cost control at M.I.T., to tackle the problem of adjusting inventory supply to demand in the transformer plant at Sharon, Pennsylvania. The job only sounds easy. Inventories of distribution transformers, which are mass produced, had a habit of piling up unless demand was estimated correctly.

Emery and his associates resorted to simulations of demand based on such things as historical buying cycles, abnormal regional growth, and interest-rate levels. They fed the data into an I.B.M. 705, which forecast demand by size, type, and location. Thus simulating demand on a weekly basis, they sharply reduced inventories while giving customers better service. "We replaced a lot of discussion over the conference table with the computer," says Hague. "If we had known years before what we learned in 1958, we would have saved millions."

Don Burnham, the president of Westinghouse and then manufacturing vice president, was enthusiastic about the computer experiment from the start. In 1960, owing to his support, the business-systems department was founded, and plans were made for the Tele-Computer Center. Inventory control is now only part of a large-scale simulation operation that relates factory operation to buying patterns. At the Tele-Computer Center two Sperry Rand Univac 490's link 360 offices, factories, and warehouses in real time. They handle an average of 2,000 orders a day. Not only do they prepare invoices and bookkeep all transactions, they send incoming orders to the nearest warehouse, and pick the next nearest warehouse if (as is unlikely) the nearest is out of the item they are looking for. Because they automatically adjust warehouse stocks to optimum level by sending a reorder to the factory, they have enabled the company to close six of its twenty-six warehouses and to slash inventories by roughly 35 percent as well as to provide better service.

Like many commercial real-time installations, this one uses a standby computer to take over if the on-line machine fails. The standby computer solves engineering problems, turns out payrolls and annual-report figures, pays dividends, and prepares various financial and sales data. This sort of chore, however, can also be done by the on-line computer. Given an urgent query, say one asking if there is a left-handed pink refrigerator in stock, the on-line computer interrupts its routine duties to answer the question or even to make out an order and appropriately adjust inventory. But then it goes right back to the routine job it was doing.

Simulation is a standard procedure at Westinghouse. In scheduling its work, for example, the management of the South Philadelphia turbine plant draws up dozens of alternative plans. Given the plans plus the actual orders on hand and the sequence in which they must be filled, the computer runs through the equivalent of two or three years of operation, and so helps decide on the best schedule. "It often only verifies our hunches," says Hague. "But it can be a real shocker at times." Simulation is also being used to evaluate plant sites and appraise other capital investment, but the most effective use of the technique will occur after more activities or "transactions" have been put on real time.

Westinghouse is now augmenting order and inventory control with production control. In its Elmira, New York, electronic-tube plant and in its South Philadelphia turbine plant the company is installing electronic data-gathering equipment that keeps accurate and timely records of various stages of production; Westinghouse estimates that such systems will pay off at 50 percent.

While all this is going on, the business-systems department keeps its eye on the goal: shrink the management information cycle. To this end it has developed what it claims is a unique technique for retrieving information from a computer's memory. So-called random-access devices, which are standard peripheral equipment, enable a man to retrieve specific facts. But when he wants to find *all* the relevant information on a given subject, random-access devices don't help much. Business systems' solution to the problem, oversimplified considerably, is to instruct the computer to file information under dozens of different headings, and then to use a "list processor" to retrieve the information by scanning appropriate categories serially. Suppose, for example, an official wants to find out how many Westinghouse people working in cryogenics have done graduate work at M.I.T. Working against three variables, the computer would have to labor through the whole random-access file to come up with the answer. But using the processor, it is back with the reply in twelve minutes: two out of 117,000 employees.

Management in the 1980's

HAROLD J. LEAVITT AND
THOMAS C. WHISLER

Harold Leavitt is Professor of Industrial Administration at the Graduate School of Industrial Administration at Carnegie Institute of Technology. Thomas Whisler is Professor of Industrial Relations at the University of Chicago's Graduate School of Business. This item is taken from their paper in the Harvard Business Review, *December 1958.*

Over the last decade a new technology has begun to take hold in American business, one so new that its significance is still difficult to evaluate. While many aspects of this technology are uncertain, it seems clear that it will move into the managerial scene rapidly, with definite and far-reaching impact on managerial organization. We would like to speculate about these effects, especially as they apply to medium-size and large business firms of the future.

The new technology does not yet have a single established name. We shall call it *information technology*. It is composed of several related parts. One includes techniques for processing large amounts of information rapidly, and it is epitomized by the high-speed computer. A second part centers around the application of statistical and mathematical methods to decision-making problems; it is represented by techniques like mathematical programing, and by methodologies like operations research. A third part is in the offing, though its applications have not yet emerged very clearly; it consists of the simulation of higher-order thinking through computer programs.

Information technology is likely to have its greatest impact on middle and top management. In many instances it will lead to opposite conclusions from those dictated by the currently popular philosophy of "participative" management. Broadly, our prognostications are along the following lines:

1. Information technology should move the boundary between planning and performance upward. Just as planning was taken from the hourly worker and given to the industrial engineer, we now expect it to be taken from a number of middle managers and given to as yet largely nonexistent specialists: "operations researchers," perhaps, or "organizational analysts." Jobs at today's middle-management level will become highly structured. Much more of the work will be programed, i.e., covered by sets of operating rules governing the day-to-day decisions that are made.

2. Correlatively, we predict that large industrial organizations will recentralize, that top managers will take on an even larger proportion of the innovating, planning, and other "creative" functions than they have now.

3. A radical reorganization of middle-management levels should occur, with *certain classes* of middle-management jobs moving downward in status and compensation (because they will require less autonomy and skill), while other classes move upward into the top-management group.

4. We suggest, too, that the line separating the top from the middle of the organization will be drawn more clearly and impenetrably than ever, much like the line drawn in the last few decades between hourly workers and first-line supervisors.

The Corporation: Will It Be Managed by Machines?

HERBERT A. SIMON

Herbert A. Simon is Associate Dean of the Graduate School of Industrial Administration at Carnegie Institute of Technology. This article is taken from his paper in Management and Corporations, 1985, *published in 1960.*

I don't know whether the title assigned to me was meant seriously or humorously. I shall take it seriously. During the past five years, I have been too close to machines—the kinds of machines known as computers, that is—to treat the question lightly. Perhaps I have lost my sense of humor and perspective about them.

My work on this paper has been somewhat impeded, in recent days, by a fascinating spectacle just outside my office window. Men and machines have been constructing the foundations of a small building. After some preliminary skirmishing by men equipped with surveying instruments and sledges for driving pegs, most of the work has been done by various species of mechanical elephant and their mahouts. Two kinds of elephants dug out the earth (one with its forelegs, the other with its trunk) and loaded it in trucks (pack elephants, I suppose). Then, after an interlude during which another group of men carefully fitted some boards into place as forms, a new kind of elephant appeared, its belly full of concrete which it disgorged into the forms. It was assisted by two men with wheelbarrows —plain old-fashioned man-handled wheelbarrows—and two or three other men who fussily tamped the poured concrete with metal rods. Twice during this whole period a shovel appeared —on one occasion it was used by a man to remove dirt that had been dropped on a sidewalk; on another occasion it was used to clean a trough down which the concrete slid.

Here, before me, was a sample of automated, or semiautomated production. What did it show about the nature of present and future relations of man with machine in the production of goods and services? And what lessons that could be learned from the automation of manufacturing and construction could be transferred to the problems of managerial automation? I concluded that there were two good reasons for beginning my analysis with a careful look at factory and office automation. First, the business organization in 1985 will be a highly automated man-machine system, and the nature of management will surely be conditioned by the character of the system being managed. Second, perhaps there are greater similarities than appear at first blush among the several areas of potential automation— blue-collar, clerical, and managerial. Perhaps the automated executive of the future has a great deal in common with the automated worker or clerk whom we can already observe in many situations today.

First, however, we must establish a framework and a point of view. Our task is to forecast the changes that will take place over the next generation in the job of the manager. It is fair to ask: Which manager? Not everyone nor every job will be affected in the same way; indeed, most persons who will be affected are not even managers at the present time. Moreover, we must distinguish the gross effects of a technological change, occurring at the point of impact of that change, from the net effects, the whole series of secondary ripples spreading from that point of initial impact.

Many of the initial effects are transitory—important enough to those directly involved at the time and place of change, but of no lasting significance to the society. Other effects are neither apparent nor anticipated when the initial change takes place but flow from it over a period of years through the succession of reactions it produces. Examples of both transient and indirect effects of change come to mind readily enough—e.g., the unemployment of blacksmiths and the appearance of suburbia, respectively, as effects of the automobile.

Since our task is to look ahead twenty-five years, I shall say little about the transient effects of the change in the job of the manager. I do not mean to discount the importance of these effects to the people they touch. In our time we are highly conscious of the transient effects, particularly the harmful ones, the displacement of skill and status. We say less of the benefit to those who acquire the new skills or of the exhilaration that many derive from erecting new structures.

Of course, the social management of change does not consist simply in balancing beneficial transient effects against harmful ones. The simplest moral reasoning leads to a general rule for the introduction of change: The general society which stands to benefit from the change should pay the major costs of introducing it and should compensate generously those who would otherwise be harmed by it. A discussion of the transient effects of change would have to center on ways of applying that rule. But that is not the problem we have to deal with here.

Our task is to forecast the long-run effects of change. First of all, we must predict what is likely to happen to the job of the individual manager, and to the activity of management in the individual organization. Changes in these patterns will have secondary effects on the occupational profile in the economy as a whole. Our task is to picture the society after it has made all these secondary adjustments and settled down to its new equilibrium. * * *

PREDICTING LONG-RUN EQUILIBRIUM

To predict long-run equilibrium, one must identify two major aspects of the total situation: (1) the variables that will change autonomously and inexorably—the "first causes"—and (2) the constant, unchanging "givens" in the situation, to which the other variables must adjust themselves. These are the hammer and the anvil that beat out the shape of the future. The accuracy of our predictions will depend less upon forecasting exactly the course of change than upon assessing correctly which factors are the unmoved movers and which the equally unmoved invariants. My entire forecast rests on my identification of this hammer and this anvil.

The Causes of Change · The growth in human knowledge is the primary factor that will give the system its direction—in particular, that will fix the boundaries of the technologically feasible. The growth in real capital is the major secondary factor in change—within the realm of what is technologically feasible, it will determine what is economical.

The crucial area of expansion of knowledge is not hard to predict, for the basic innovations—or at least a large part of them—have already occurred and we are now rapidly exploiting them. The new knowledge consists in a fundamental understanding of the processes of thinking and learning or, to use a more neutral term, of complex information processing. We can now write programs for electronic computers that enable these devices to think and learn. This knowledge is having, and will have, practical impacts in two directions: (1) because we can now simulate in considerable detail an important and increasing part of the processes of the human mind, we have available a technique of tremendous power for psychological research; (2) because we can now write complex information-processing programs for computers, we are acquiring the technical capacity to replace humans with computers in a rapidly widening range of "thinking" and "deciding" tasks.

Closely allied to the development of complex information-processing techniques for general-purpose computers is the rapid advance in the technique of automating all sorts of production and clerical tasks. Putting these two lines of development together, I am led to the following general predictions: Within the very near future—much less than twenty-five years—we shall have the *technical* capability of substituting machines for any and all human functions in organizations. Within the same period, we shall have acquired an extensive and empirically tested theory of human cognitive processes and their interaction with human emotions, attitudes, and values.

To predict that we will have these technical capabilities says nothing of how we shall use them. Before we can forecast that, we must discuss the important invariants in the social system.

The Invariants · The changes that our new technical capability will bring about will be governed, particularly in the production sphere, by two major fixed factors in the society. Both of these have to do with the use of human resources for production.

1. Apart from transient effects of automation, the human resources of the society will be substantially fully employed. *Full employment* does not necessarily mean a forty-hour week, for the allocation of productive capacity between additional goods and services and additional leisure may continue to change as it has in the past. *Full employment* means that the opportunity to work will be available to virtually all adults in the society and that, through wages or other allocative devices, the product of the economy will be distributed widely among families.

2. The distribution of intelligence and ability in the society will be much as it is now, although a substantially larger percentage of adults (perhaps half or more) will have completed college educations.

These assumptions—of capability of automation, accompanied by full employment and constancy in the quality of the human resources—provide us with a basis for characterizing the change. We cannot talk about the technological unemployment it may create, for we have assumed that such unemployment is a transient phenomenon—that there will be none in the long run. But the pattern of occupations, the profile showing the relative distribution of employed persons among occupations, may be greatly changed. It is the change in this profile that will measure the organizational impact of the technological change.

The change in the occupational profile depends on a well-known economic principle, the doctrine of comparative advantage. It may seem paradoxical to think that we can increase the productivity of mechanized techniques in all processes without displacing men somewhere. Won't a point be reached where men are less productive than machines in *all* processes, hence economically unemployable?[1]

1. The difficulty that laymen find with this point underlies the consistent failure of economists to win wide general support for the free trade argu-

The paradox is dissolved by supplying a missing term. Whether man or machines will be employed in a particular process depends not simply on their relative productivity in physical terms but on their cost as well. And cost depends on price. Hence—so goes the traditional argument of economics—as technology changes and machines become more productive, the prices of labor and capital will so adjust themselves as to clear the market of both. As much of each will be employed as offers itself at the market price, and the market price will be proportional to the marginal productivity of that factor. By the operation of the market place, manpower will flow to those processes in which its productivity is comparatively high relative to the productivity of machines; it will leave those processes in which its productivity is comparatively low. The comparison is not with the productivities of the past, but among the productivities in different processes with the currently available technology.

I apologize for dwelling at length on a point that is clearly enough stated in the *Wealth of Nations.* My excuse is that contemporary discussion of technological change and automation still very often falls into error through not applying the doctrine of comparative advantage correctly and consistently.

We conclude that human employment will become smaller relative to the total labor force in those kinds of occupations and activities in which automatic devices have the greatest comparative advantage over humans; human employment will become relatively greater in those occupations and activities in which automatic devices have the least comparative advantage.[2]

---

ment. The central idea—that comparative advantage, not absolute advantage, counts—is exactly the same in the two cases.

2. I am oversimplifying, for there is another term in this equation. With a general rise in productivity and with shifts in relative prices due to uneven technological progress in different spheres, the demands for some kinds of goods and services will rise more rapidly than the demands for others. Hence, other things being equal, the total demand will rise in those occupations (of men and machines) that are largely concerned with producing the former, more rapidly than in occupations concerned largely with producing the latter. I have shown elsewhere how all these mechanisms can be handled formally in analyzing technological change. See "Productivity and the Urban-Rural Population Balance," in *Models of Man* (New York, John Wiley & Sons, Inc., 1957) chapter 12; and "Effects of Technological Change in a Linear Model," in T. Koopmans (ed.), *Activity Analysis of Production and Allocation,* (New York, John Wiley & Sons, Inc., 1951) chapter 15.

Thus, if computers are a thousand times faster than book-keepers in doing arithmetic, but only one hundred times faster than stenographers in taking dictation, we shall expect the number of bookkeepers per thousand employees to decrease but the number of stenographers to increase. Similarly, if computers are a hundred times faster than executives in making investment decisions, but only ten times faster in handling employee grievances (the quality of the decisions being held constant), then computers will be employed in making investment decisions, while executives will be employed in handling grievances.